MW00784795

Penis Size and Enlargement

Facts, Fallacies and Proven Methods

Gary Griffin

Foreword by Gary W. Rheinschild, M.D.

HOURGLASS
BOOK PUBLISHING

P.O. Box 171, Aptos, CA 95001

Library of Congress Cataloging in Publication Data:

Griffin, Gary M.
     Penis Size and Enlargement
     Bibliography: p.
     Includes index.
     1. Penis   2. Sexuality.

Printed in the United States of America

ISBN #0-934061-24-6 Softcover

Contents

Contents (cont.)

Foreword

━━━━━━━━━━━━━━━━━

Ten years ago, a young man made an appointment with me for a medical evaluation. He was very cryptic when the nurse began taking his vitals, stating that the purpose of his appointment was very personal and that he only wanted to discuss it with the doctor.

A few minutes later, I tapped on the door of the examination room and entered. Chuck was a handsome young man, tall, athletic, and in his mid 20s. I introduced myself, shook hands, and briefly perused his medical chart. His vital signs were all in order.

"What can I do for you Chuck?" I inquired.

"It took all my courage to make the appointment," he began. "I couldn't even talk to the nurse about it." I assumed that he was experiencing erectile difficulties and asked if he was having problems in his marital relations. "I just got married a couple of years ago. I'm able to achieve an erection--that's not the problem--I just don't think I'm able to please my wife."

I was beginning to think that his problem would be better addressed by a sex therapist. "Why don't you feel you're able to please your wife?" I asked. He hesitated momentarily and looked at the floor in embarrassment. "I'm either very small or my wife is awfully large. We just don't have a great deal of pleasure during sex."

This wasn't the first time I had been visited by a patient who thought that his penis was too small. In fact, barely a week would go by when I didn't have to address this problem with a patient. In most cases, the concern was unwarranted and I was able to alleviate the man's anxiety, assuring him that his phallic dimensions were within the normal range. Similarly, I was prepared to examine Chuck and put him at ease.

I asked him to remove his shorts so that I might examine him. I sensed his high level of anxiety and turned away briefly to slip on a pair of latex gloves. Chuck was perched on the side of the examination table with his briefs around his ankles. "Let's see what we have here." I looked at his genitalia and was shocked to see a miniscule glans protruding from a thick tuft of dark pubic hair. He truly had an undersized penis, and I did my best to hide my surprise. I explained that I was going to take a "stretched flaccid"

5

measurement to determine his true size. I gently grasped his glans and stretched the penis, placing a ruler on top. He measured barely 4 1/4".

"Well, Chuck, about 75% of all men measure between five and seven inches when they're erect, so you're just a bit below average. But this doesn't mean that you can't enjoy sexual relations." There are many men in your size range who enjoy full and pleasurable sex lives. My advice is to learn new techniques, including manual, oral, AND penile stimulation." A few minutes later, he dressed and left. What I didn't have the heart to tell him is that he had a borderline micropenis, which really was too small to provide sufficient coital friction for many women--especially those that had borne children. But since there was nothing that could be done to increase his size, I could only suggest that he improve his technique and utilize positions that maximized contact. I sincerely wished that there was more that I could do for him, but medicine had no miracles for his situation.

A few months ago, I ran into Chuck again. He made another appointment and appeared in my office. I remembered the face, but after ten years, couldn't remember the name. In the examination room, he refreshed my memory regarding our first visit and told me that he was back because he had seen an ad about surgical penis enlargement. Indeed I assured him that I was doing the procedure and had already lengthened the penises of over 200 men. He was truly excited at the prospect of a larger penis, and although there were no guarantees, he was willing to take his chances.

I scheduled him for the outpatient procedure three weeks later. The surgery went well and he followed his post-op instructions explicitly. Two months later, he arrived for a follow-up visit. I measured his penis and proudly announced that he had gained an inch. His 5 1/4" penis was now soundly in the average range of erect penile measurements. The fat I added to his penis in the dermal fat graft procedure had also increased the circumference by more than 1 1/2".

Six weeks after his surgery, Chuck and his wife had sex. His newly-enlarged penis truly made a difference as he coyly related that his wife screamed with orgasmic pleasure for the first time. Usually he was only to able to bring her to orgasm orally, but now his penis was large enough to provide pleasurable friction. Chuck was certain that the surgery had saved his love life.

Many doctors decry surgical penis enlargement, claiming that it is technique, not size that matters. They are right when they claim that it isn't always successful. But for those whose penises have been successfully enlarged, their quality of life has immeasurably improved. One noted doctor commented that the penis is the very embodiment of a man's ego--and a larger penis goes a long way to increasing a man's self-esteem and perceived virility. And nothing is more precious and valuable to a man.

Gary W. Rheinschild, MD

Introduction

Are we the unwitting victims of a sexual conspiracy? If not, then is there any logical reason why Western Society considers the subject of the male genitals anathema?

Our culture is redolent with duplicitous sexual mores. Take fashion, for example. While it is considered acceptable (and indeed elegant) for a decolleté-clad woman to expose her cleavage or reveal all but the most intimate parts of her anatomy in a string bikini, a man's privates, however, are just that--private, hidden, and obscured in mystery as if they don't (or shouldn't) exist. To conform to puritanical standards of decency, male statues are modestly draped with an obligatory fig leaf while men modeling underwear for print ads are carefully "arranged" so as to not display any suggestive bulge. After all, we wouldn't want anyone to know that he actually had a penis, would we?

Nudity on screen has become more widely accepted in the past decade, but such tolerance generally applies only to the female anatomy. It is rare nowadays to see a movie in which the actress doesn't expose her breasts and derriere during a love scene, yet when is the last time the leading man was similarly revealed? The only instances that come to mind are *Basic Instinct* and *The Crying Game.* Yet these hardly qualify as mainstream representations of normalcy considering that the penis revealed in the former belonged to a dead man who was brutally slashed with an icepick and the latter dangled from the loins of a transvestite! Bruce Willis, however, did break cinematographic ground when he insisted that his full frontal nude scene in *The Color of Night* be retained for the video version.

7

My estimation is that the frank discussion of the male genitalia is a firecracker of an issue that threatens to expose potentially-discomforting truths to many men. Yet, that is specifically the reason why we as men need to be informed of the truth of our sexual equipment. Today, ignorance reigns supreme as the uncontested culprit of human problems, misunderstanding, and misery. And as long as men are kept in the dark about their sexual organs, they will continue to harbor misconceptions about themselves and suffer from anxiety, confusion, and sexual inadequacy.

This book is an attempt to shed some academic light on a subject that has been traditionally imbued with mythology, ignorance, and a dearth of hard scientific data. Most men are secretly curious about how they compare to others. Many of us wonder, "Is my penis smaller or larger than average?" "How do I compare sexually with other men?," or "Can I really increase the size of my penis?" Knowledge is power, and the more men know about their bodies and sexual functions, the greater will be their confidence in sexual performance. If a man suspects that his penis is small, but has no access to reliable scientific data, he will confirm his own suspicions by convincing himself that he IS small. But if the same man finds out that his 5" penis is well within the range of normal penis sizes, it may completely alter his self-image.

Anxiety over penis size is one of the most common causes of sexual dysfunction, yet for fear of offending the puritanical sensibilities of the fundamentalist and "born again" segments of our society, the topic of penis size as it contributes to male sexual performance is still enshrouded by a titanic miasma of suspicion.

When the sexual revolution emerged, people everywhere began searching for the truth about their bodies. In the 1960s we questioned authority and the values of our parents. In the 1970s, we experimented with sexuality. In the 1980s, the swing back to conservativism awakened a renewed interest in our health and concern about the substances we take into our bodies. Now, in the 1990s, our view is more global in scope and we are beginning to understand the macro consequences of acid rain, the greenhouse effect, toxins in the food chain, and the burdens of overpopulation on the environment.

People are now demanding honest answers to important questions. Do the pesticides in our foods cause cancer? Is nuclear energy really safe? How does the destruction of the tropical rain forests affect the planet's future? Is the U.S. Government deliberately squelching knowledge of UFO encounters?

While some myopic segments of Americana yearn to return to the blissful ignorance of the 1950s with its Doris Day innocense, poodle skirts, and Father-Knows-Best chauvinism, we are as a whole, a better informed and less-passive people who demand truthful answers to important questions. For that reason, men are anxious to learn the truth about their genitals. But where do they turn?

This book is written to provide accurate information on a subject that has too often been considered "obscene" and "off limits." As it is important to understand the etiology of cancer in order to produce therapies to fight the disease, it is also important for men to understand their genitals and their function in order to gain maximum pleasure and satisfaction from them. It is hoped that this information will put many men at ease, while providing hope for other men who are dissatisfied with the size and performance of their genitals and wish to improve them.

Although the overall tone of this book is meant to be academic, I wanted to have some fun with it as well. For that reason, I have included the chapter on well-endowed celebrities. When I have appeared on talkshows, this topic has always garnered the greatest amount of interest. "Who has the biggest cock in Hollywood?" is the most popular question. You'll find the answer to this and much more in chapter six.

New research has revealed fascinating details about enlargement rituals found in such far-flung locations as Kashmir, Tibet, Peru, and the Sudan. We'll explore these in detail in chapter seven. You'll also read case histories of several of my readers who have recently undergone penis enlargement programs. And in chapter three, I've included some brand new information that graphically illustrates the distribution of penis sizes among adults.

I hope you enjoy the book and that it answers some of the questions you've always been too embarrassed to ask. If you find any inaccuracies or wish to enlighten me on an interesting aspect of male sexuality, or to share a success story, please write to me directly at 100 S. Sunrise Way, Suite #484, Palm Springs, CA 92263. All of your correspondence is read and is greatly appreciated. Without further ado, read on and have FUN!

Gary Griffin
Palm Springs, February 1995

PENILE ENLARGEMENT

LAST YEAR 300,000 MEN CALLED OUR MEDICAL GROUP.

FACT Average patient increases in length 1"-2" and 30%-50% in circumference.

FACT Surgery requires about 1 1/2 hours on an outpatient basis.

FACT The results are immediate.

FACT 70% of our patients are of average size to begin.

SOME OF OUR PATIENTS INCLUDE MAJOR MOTION PICTURE STARS, RECORDING ARTISTS, T.V. PERSONALITIES, ENTERTAINERS, AND PROFESSIONAL ATHLETES.

OUR PATIENTS ARE FROM ALL 50 STATES AND OVER 35 FOREIGN COUNTRIES.

As one patient said to the phisician, "Come on Doc, what man wouldn't want an extra 2 inches?"

Dreams <u>Do</u> Come True!

Surgicare has medical offices throughout the U.S. Call today for a FREE consultation or a full color brochure.

———

(800)_____

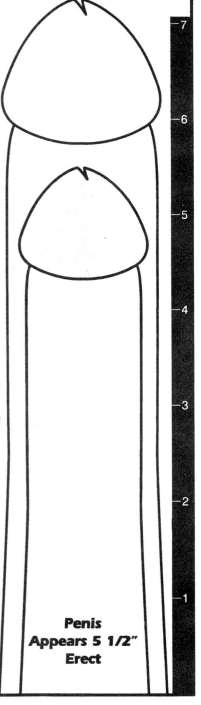

Same Penis increased by 1 1/2" length & 50% in Circumference

Penis Appears 5 1/2" Erect

Some ads make highly exaggerated claims. This one and others like it appeared in Penthouse magazine.

1

A matter of inches

QUESTION: If it were truly possible, would you like to add an inch or two in length and/or girth to your penis?

If you have ever entertained the fantasy of possessing a larger penis, stay tuned...this book is for you. In the following pages, we will explore the size of the average penis, reveal the largest penises ever recorded in medical annals, and discuss the variation in size among the races. We'll also present research into the various methods of penis enlargement that have been practiced over the centuries.

Man's quest for a larger penis is more of a global obsession than you might realize. Primitive man often suspended heavy stones from his penis in an attempt to lengthen it, and post-Renaissance European fashion dictated that sartorially-savvy gentlemen don padded codpieces to enhance the illusion of a large penis.

If you suspect that most penis enlargement methods are bogus, you are absolutely right. However, modern research has revealed several methods which show great promise in increasing the size of a man's natural endowment. More recently, two new surgical procedures have been

---

❑   The average adult penis in the flaccid state is 9.5 cm. (4").

introduced for increasing the girth and length of the penis. In the following pages, we'll investigate the various methods of penis enlargement and separate fact from "phallusy."

In the 10 years that I have been investigating male sexuality, I have come across dozens of purported methods of penis enlargement, ranging from the logical to the ridiculous. Along the way, I have met a coterie of intelligent researchers who share a fascination for this subject. Together we have investigated every possible method and have reached conclusions about their degree of effectiveness (or uselessness). The results are presented in chapter seven.

A donkey in the sauna

In the early 1980s, I was conducting postgraduate work at UCLA. The academic load was monstrous, so to help alleviate the mental strain, I participated in a regular regimen of arduous physical activity. On Tuesday evenings, Bob, my gym partner, and I regularly engaged in a strenuous four-game set of racquetball at the local health spa. Afterward, we enjoyed a hot, stinging shower punctuated by a trip to the sauna to relax our muscles. Being of Scandinavian heritage, I learned to appreciate the salubrious effects of a good hot sauna at an early age. With eucalyptus-scented water splashed on the sizzling coals, the swirling steam would bring out the aromatic muskiness of the redwood paneling. The heated mixture provided the perfect antidote for sore muscles and stiff joints aggravated by athletic overindulgence.

Dripping with perspiration, Bob and I quickly stripped after one particularly exhausting game, tossed our sweaty gym gear in our lockers, and headed for the showers. Summoning up reserves of macho bravado, we both jumped in the ice plunge for a bone-chilling dip, then raced into the heated sanctuary of the sauna, perching ourselves on the uppermost bench to take advantage of the rising steam. As we settled down and dried the final beads of icy water from our torsos, the door opened.

I instantly recognized the figure in the doorway as the star running back for the Bruins--UCLA's nationally-ranked football team. A towering figure of six-foot-four, he sported the body of a latter-day Adonis, with

❏   Although there is great variation, the average adult penis increases 7.5 cm. (3") during erection.

handsome, with sculpted facial features reminiscent of Tom Cruise. Needless to say, he was a favorite among the coeds. With the body of a muscled Michelangelo statue and the face of a matinee idol, it was no small wonder he recently graced the cover of *Sports Illustrated.* His entrance attracted a few cursory glances of admiration, and he offered a patronizing nod to a pair of appreciative underclassmen, then sat down on the front bench as everyone nonchalantly resumed their private conversations.

Scarcely a minute later, the door swung open again. Mouths dropped in astonishment and eyes blinked in disbelief. The guy in the doorway was not another Adonis--not by any stretch of the imagination. A stout and scrawny fellow, he sported a mop of coarse unruly hair accented by a prominent aquiline nose on which teetered a pair of thick-lensed spectacles. His body was even less remarkable, with a sunken, hairless chest and underdeveloped muscles. Yet there was one particularly outstanding characteristic which made my sauna companions ignore the homely facial features. He brandished a pendulously long and thick penis which dangled like a firehose between his legs. In street clothes, he would have been branded the campus nebbish, but in the buff, he commanded the immediate attention of everyone around.

He seated himself on the lower bench next to the All-American Running Back, making absolutely no attempt to conceal his monument to manhood. He was clearly proud of his mule-sized trophy and appeared genuinely delighted that he had generated such interest. There were at least a dozen men in the sauna and I looked around in amusement as each one discreetly craned his neck to get a glimpse of that incredible phallus. I was absolutely transfixed, wondering if I had ever seen a larger one. I doubt if I had. It seemed a foot long. All conversation ceased, and one could almost hear the collective thoughts whispering, "Look at the mammoth meathose on that guy--what a lucky man!"

The football player realized that he had been unmercifully upstaged by a far less-attractive physical specimen, which clearly made him uncomfortable. I watched in amusement as he ogled the donkey dick next to him through the corner of his eye. I had to stifle a small snicker as he reached for his rumpled towel and covered his own peanut-sized putz in conciliatory embarrassment. He was living proof of the axiom "the bigger the muscles, the smaller the meat." I guess he realized he was no longer king of the

❏   The genitals of the male generally reach adult proportions around age 17.

13

locker room. As Mr. Firehose began to build up a sweat, he casually tossed his towel over his shoulder, arose from the bench, and unceremoniously paraded past us on his way to the shower, offering ample opportunity for all to silently admire his imposing plumbing. Was our interest kindled by feelings of admiration, respect, or envy? Judging by the intense visual interest that he created, I'm sure that it was a combination of all three.

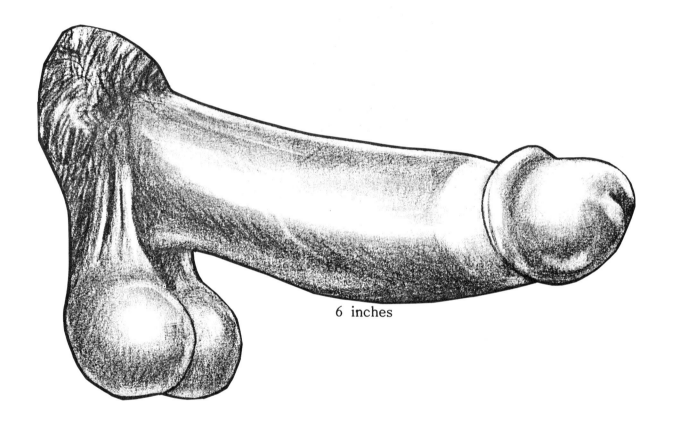

6 inches

❏   75% of all adult males sport erections that measure between 5 and 7 inches (12.5 - 17.5 cm).

2

The advantages of size

In a perfect world, physical characteristics should not matter. One's height, weight, nose shape, bone structure, or penis size shouldn't be cause for either disdain or praise. Indeed, a man with a small penis who happens to be happy and contented nonetheless is worthy of adulation. Noted Los Angeles urologist Dudley Seth Danoff, M.D., author of the best-seller *Superpotency,* tries to instill a sense of pride in every man, regardless of his endowment status. In a letter written to one of my readers seeking advice about penis enlargement surgery, Dr. Danoff writes:

> I am adamantly opposed to any penile enlargement operations, as they do not make any anatomic, psychological or medical sense. I have been in urologic practice for more than 20 years and have examined more than 100,000 penises, and I can assure you with great certainty that the only thing that counts is the ability to get it erect.

However, the world places a premium (perhaps unfairly so) on certain shapes and sizes of body parts. The penis is no exception. And even though Dr. Danoff steadfastly maintains his position that "one size fits all," he does concede in his letter that "If YOU think it is important that you have a large penis, then it IS important, just as some men favor large breasted women."

❏ In a recent issue of *Glamour* magazine, 3000 men were asked if there were a surgery that could increase the size of the penis, would they go for it? 33% reponded "yes." If the surgery were painless and free, doubtless the response would have been much higher.

15

Is bigger better?

What specifically is there about a large, well-developed penis that commands the immediate attention and arousal of both sexes? It is likely a combination of atavistic and psychological factors. In primitive societies, the man with the biggest muscles, the most extensive herd, and the largest shelter commanded more power and prestige than his lesser-equipped fellow tribesmen. By sheer size and power he became the dominant force in the clan. In these tribal cultures, the male organ was viewed as the root of procreation, and therefore, the symbol of dominance. Bigness became synonymous with superiority--consequently the man with the largest penis became the tribal object of admiration, worship, and respect.

A large penis carries the unmistakable connotation of power. In *The Durable Fig Leaf*, ethnologist Wolfgang Wickler comments that "psychoanalysts are in danger of overlooking the fact that the phallus...is a symbol of power." In their groundbreaking book, *Human Sexual Response,* Masters and Johnson remark that "The size of the male organ both in flaccid and erect state has been presumed by many cultures to reflect directly the sexual prowess of the individual male."

It may be a fair premise to theorize that the rise of phallicism and the fascination with the large penis can be traced to the equating of masculinity, dominance, and power with "bigness." The notion that "bigger is better" lingers with us today, so we might as well accept the fact (although not politically correct) that the genuinely large phallus is not only appealing from an aesthetic aspect, it also inspires awe and respect from the beholder, and instills a genuine sense of pride in the possessor.

A cursory linguistic examination of the English term "well-endowed" speaks volumes. Funk & Wagnall's Standard Dictionary defines "endowed" as "furnished or equipped as with natural talents or gifts"--certainly a desirable attribute in anybody's book. And of course, the adverb "well" connotes a favorable state, as in "well-spoken," "well-dressed," and well-behaved." Likewise, the colloquialism "well-endowed" contains a subliminal tip-of-the-hat to the desirability of a large organ. It is interesting to note that the term has a direct equivalent in virtually all Indo-European languages, meaning that it was likely coined by speakers of the aboriginal Proto-Indo European tongue thousands of years ago and still carries a

❏ A male in a high degree of sexual excitement is capable of ejaculating his semen 24" (0.7 meters) or greater.

16

favorable connotation among cultures around the globe. Were the presence of a large penis viewed as a hindrance or liability, our ancestors would have likely coined the term "encumbered," or "burdened."

Phallicism in history

Early cultures were much more open in their expression of admiration for the penis. The Hindus were particularly appreciative of the large phallus. Their artwork and sculptures abound with images of horse-hung men. Ironically, the worship of the large penis extended only to images and icons. In the human, however, the small penis was esteemed as the epitome of manhood. The *Kama Sutra* identifies four types of males by the size of the penis. The "Shushah" (hare man) with an erect penis of only 2-3" (5-7 cm) is characterized as "lithe and strong," and the "beau ideal." The mid-sized man, or the "Mrigah" (buck man) is described as "the perfection of warriors. He is fleet and graceful" with an erect penis measuring 4-6" (10-15 cm). The man with the large 7-8" (18-20 cm) penis is referred to as "Vrishubha" (bull man), being characterized as "tough and muscular." The lowest man on the totem pole, the "Ushvah" (stallion man) was the rare individual with a wrist-thick, taurine tumescence measuring greater than 9" (23 cm). The Hindus sardonically considered such a man "worthless and indolent."

The Greeks were the other culture of note that expressed a dichotomy in their admiration of the penis. Their gods are often massively-endowed while humans were depicted with puny penises. If you feel you're underendowed, take heart, you would have been a big hit in ancient Athens. Large penises were perceived to be abnormal and ungainly, and were banished to the domains of caricature, satyrs, or barbarians. In explaining the Hellenic predilection for small genitals, Aristotle reasoned that the short penis was more fertile than a long one, because the semen had a shorter distance to travel and didn't cool off as much during ejaculation. We now know that such reasoning was folly, and apart from the Greeks and Hindus, virtually all other cultures (including our own), venerate the large penis.

The Arab fascination with the large phallus can be summed up by the old Moslem maxim that a woman "prefers an additional inch of penis to anything this world or the next might offer." So obsessed were the Arabs with

❏   On a diet? Semen has only five calories per teaspoon.

17

notions of the superiority of the large penis that the Ottoman Turks conquered them in part on the strength of the Turks' perceived phallic superiority. The Turks publicly posted the measurements of the vanquished Arab leaders, comparing them to the real or imagined superior cock sizes of the Turkish commanders. This helped to effectively shatter Arab resistance.

In the far East, the exaggerated penis is the focal point of many Japanese "pillow books," which are an Oriental version of erotic material, employed for centuries as a visual aphrodisiac. In post-Renaissance Europe, it became fashionable for males to wear codpieces, which were primitive jockstraps sewed to the outside of the male costume and designed to

Typical illustration from a Japanese "pillow book" placing particular emphasis on the exaggerated male genitalia.

❑   In 1955, archaeologists on the Mediterranean island of Corsica stumbled upon Bronze Age phallic monuments standing 6-10' high.

18

emphasize the bulge of the male anatomy. Men of modest endowment often compensated by padding their codpieces with handkerchiefs, coins, and keys. Full-body portraits of Napolean clearly demonstrate his predilection for amply-padded codpieces. Regardless of the culture or era, one thing is for certain. Almost every society esteems the large penis as the hallmark of male superiority.

Body image problems

The immortal Scottish poet, Robert Burns, once expressed the desire for men to be able to see themselves as others see them. This disparity between perception and reality (do others see the same body that I see when I look in the mirror?) generates what Dr. Felix Grange refers to as "body image problems." These problems occur because there is a perceptual gap between the way we look and the way we wished we looked.

Few people are genuinely satisfied with their physical appearance. Even many of the glamorous, immaculately-coiffed starlets that grace the covers of fashion magazines are critical of their looks. In Hollywood, a community where physical perfection is a prized commodity, a surprising number of media darlings have undergone some sort of surgical enhancement or reconstruction. Thanks to this perception of physical inadequacy, plastic surgery has become a thriving business. Tummy tucks, face lifts, nose-bobs, and liposuction are all surgical testaments to the obsessive quest for eternal youth and physical perfection.

Bigness as a symbol of sexual desirability is by no means limited to the male. Large, voluptuous breasts have become such an obsession in the psyche of the Western male that many women have resorted to surgical breast augmentation in order to bolster their sense of femininity and desirability. Dolly, Liz, and Bette are all symbols of the male fascination for cleavage and decolletage. Fortunately, if we are dissatisfied with our physical appearance, modern medicine has provided high-tech methods for erasing nature's inequities. Facial wrinkles can be magically smoothed with collagen or Retin-A, birthmarks skillfully erased by medical lasers, and unattractive or aquiline noses can be artfully reconstructed. All it takes is a small bankroll and a skilled plastic surgeon.

❏   In Biblical times, Hebrew tribes held the male genitalia and its procreative powers in such high regard that oaths were sworn on the penis, much as we swear on the Bible today.

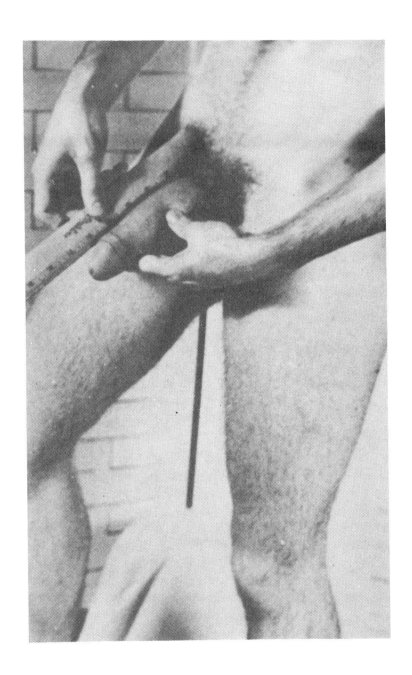

This impressive penis measures 7" when flaccid. Most men are not this long when erect.

Men, though, are plagued by several physical shortcomings that aren't so easily remedied. Weight can be controlled through dieting, exercise, and medication. A weak, underdeveloped body can be fortified with bulging muscles and impressive definition through regular exercise. But certain areas of the male anatomy still evoke great trepidation. These three problem areas are height, baldness, and penis size.

Substandard stature is primarily an annoyance only to the man who is short. It seldom bothers his friends or loved ones. Baldness is another sensitive subject. Most men fear the loss of their hair, subliminally equating it with declining virility. But no aspect of the male anatomy arouses greater anxiety than penis size.

Anxiety over penis size

Why is this concern with genital size of such paramount importance to men? Simply put, the penis is the very embodiment of a man's ego, and most men fear that they are small. Men often consider the size of the penis to be a barometer of virility. Phillip B. Luloff, M.D., a sex therapist and assistant professor of psychiatry at Mount Sinai Hospital in New York City says that "when you're measuring the size of your penis, the instrument you're using is not a ruler but some assessment of your self esteem." Dr. Felix Grange succinctly illustrates the psychological importance that a man attaches to his penis:

> To call a man a liar, a fool, a cheat, may offend him. To ridicule his genitals is to strike at the very core of his image. A man fears he is small. To tell him so and confirm his fears can be to deal him a shattering blow.

Psychotherapists and sex researchers generally agree that anxiety over penis size is one of the primary causes of situational impotence. Dr. Luloff says that "in the extreme, a man's anxiety about the size and shape of his penis can affect his sexual functioning. But even if such a man appears to be functioning normally, concern about his endowment might still cause him much distress. Both his self-image and self-esteem suffer." Dr. Morton Walker agrees: "In my opinion, if men knew more about their genitals and the normal sexual response, a lot less impotence would prevail."

❏   In 16th century England, men wore a braquette (codpiece) which was like a padded jockstrap. This caused a conspicuous bulge in the trousers and was intended as a visual aphrodisiac. The largest codpiece on display at the Tower of London allegedly belonged to Henry VIII.

21

Anxiety over penis size arises from a series of unresolved questions and doubts. For that reason, I suggest that the man who knows the facts of genital size and its possible significance is better equipped to cope with his "shortcomings" than someone who lacks the facts and continually worries over this perceived deficiency. The man who knows the facts will also be better able to make decisions regarding penis enlargement. As we will soon see, large genitals are not a requisite for satisfactory sexual relations, but a large penis has certain inherent advantages over a small organ.

Why do men attach such importance to the size of the penis? Simply stated, men are competitive creatures. In various aspects of a man's life--whether it be his job, education, or income--there is a subliminal pecking order that establishes his status in relation to other men. A large penis firmly assures a man's place near the top of the virility totem pole. Men and women alike perceive the man with the large penis to be more powerful and virile. A small penis is seldom viewed as an asset in the psyche of the male. Psychiatrist Gifford Chase Ph.D, author of *Sex in the Fast Lane* theorizes that men with small and average-sized penises suffer from feelings of inadequacy all their lives.

> A man's phallus is unquestionably his most prized possession. A small or short penis is more humiliating to a male than a Cyrano-sized nose or early baldness. Men with even average intelligence realize intellectually that most females feel more pain than pleasure during coitus with an overly-endowed male. But penis size involves a male's emotions, not his intellect; an outsized organ is a badge of emotional merit, which, if absent, makes him feel he is somehow a failure as a man. Males have been emotionally involved with penis size since prehistoric times; carvings on the walls of caves depict males with penises as large as the clubs they carried.

Psychiatrist Ron Podell, M.D., director of the Center for Mood Disorders in Los Angeles, says that the prominence of the penis makes it "a very convenient place for a man to focus a lot of his insecurity about his maleness and attractiveness, so it becomes a focus of negative comparison." Boys start making comparisons with their peers during puberty when pubic hair begins to sprout and penises start to develop. Throughout adulthood, locker room and restroom comparisons continue, either reinforcing or allaying the man's fear about his endowment status.

❑   A punishment occasionally inflicted upon an adulterous male by the ancient Greeks consisted of shaving his pubic hair and inserting a large radish in his rectum.

The problem with these comparisons is that they occur with other flaccid penises. From a biological and functional standpoint, the only measurement that counts is the erect penis--and a limp organ offers scant indication of how it will look at full staff. Just as a limp organ is no indication of its erect size potential, neither is the view from which men observe their own penises. Looking down at one's own penis makes is look foreshortened, thereby reinforcing the fear of a substandard-sized organ.

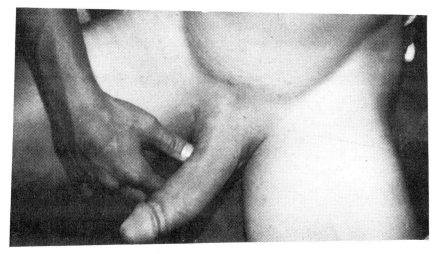

A large, well-developed phallus can go a long way to providing sexual pleasure to both partners.

In *The Penis*, Dr. Dick Richards encapsulates the precise reasons why men esteem large penises on themselves--and on others:

> Penis size matters to a man. It is one of his great pride centres. Much of his ego is in, or is at least supported by, his penis. As long as men think, wish, and hope that the size of the penis really counts, then it does. That is the be-all and end-all of the argument. Their minds are made up. It is useless confusing them with facts. The whole thing speaks for itself. Men have decided, believed and been conditioned into a way of thinking that accepts penis size as of supreme relevance. So there all fruitful discussion and argument might as well end. If men are convinced that it counts...it does.

___

❑ Napolean Bonaparte's sister, Pauline, was a notorious nymphomaniac with a predilection for huge cocks. An affair with the hugely-hung Italian painter, Nicholas Philippe Auguste de Forbin, continued until she began suffering from "vaginal distress."

If you feel that your penis is smaller than you'd like it to be, you are in good company. Dr. Barry McCarthy, author of *Male Sexual Awareness,* found that two out of three men believe that their penises are smaller than average. And penis size is the second most popular area of concern among males (following impotence) who contact the Kinsey Institute for help. In the *Journal of the American Medical Association,* Dr. James F. Glenn echoes this concern, remarking "It can be safely said that the adult male population suffers an almost universal anxiety in regard to penile size." This universal concern with penis size was clearly exposed in an issue of *Medical Aspects of Human Sexuality.* A monthly feature of this esteemed publication is a "Dear Doctor" column which attempts to resolve frequently-asked sexual questions posed by patients. A recently-submitted question asked:

> Your patient is concerned that his penis is too small. What advice should you give him?'

The physician was then invited to call a toll-free number for the answer. When I dialed the number, I was greeted by the following recorded message: "Due to an overwhelming response to this question, this answer is no longer being offered." The phone lines were apparently jammed from the deluge of incoming calls. The editorial staff was caught off guard as they were evidently unprepared for the torrent of queries. This situation clearly underscores the fact that men are kept in the dark about penis size and performance and are ravenously hungry for honest answers.

By the way, anxiety over penis size may be directly proportional to the degree of privacy that individual societies place on the male genitalia. Europeans, for example, don't enshroud the penis in a fig leaf of mystery as do Americans, Israelis, and Arabs. Male frontal nudity in European films is common and nude beaches abound. The arrangement of men's restrooms is also a reflection of this degree of modesty. Whereas European men freely line up side-by-side to urinate against an open stainless-steel urinal, American men are quite uncomfortable having their genitals exposed to other men. Most American restrooms feature "modesty panels" between urinals to discourage subrosa viewing. This prudish sense of modesty carries over to cinematography. Steamy Hollywood movies frequently display ample amounts of female skin, yet the genitals of the male remain conveniently enshrouded. Indeed, public exposure of the penis remains the last taboo.

❏ The notorious Pope Alexander VI hosted numerous orgies. At one particular party, fifty nude prostitutes were hired to service a group of men. A prize was awarded to the man who exhibited the greatest stamina.

I postulate that if men were allowed access to the facts of genital size, many of their sexual frustrations would disappear. Most men express anxiety over penis size simply because they have not been provided with the facts. Most men would like to know:

❏   How large is the average-sized penis?

❏   What is the ''normal'' range of penis sizes?

❏   How do I compare to other men?

❏   Does size make a difference in sexual performance?

❏   Can I increase the size of my penis?

By the time you finish this book, you'll have all the answers. Vernon Bosch, author of *Sexual Dimensions: the Fact and Fiction of Genital Size* states:

> There is a great reservoir of documented, authoritative evidence to prove that incalculable human frustration, anxiety, marital disasters, and mental illnesses have their roots in ignorance and misinformation about sex in general and the sex organs in particular.

Even the sex experts agree that we have been kept in the dark about our sex organs. Masters & Johnson state that "there is no organ about which more misinformation has been perpetrated." Dr. Shak Kokken, author of the marriage guide *A Happier Sex Life* agrees: "A high percentage of men are inflicted with an inferiority complex regarding their penises." Small wonder. Most men have never seen another erect penis--or at least an average-sized one. The penises we see in pornographic videos are more likely to resemble those of stallions than of men. Just one more blow to the man's self-esteem.

Genital insecurity is evident at any athletic club. Take a look around the locker room and notice how men discreetly cover themselves on the way to the shower. You may argue that this is merely a display of modesty, but it is equally likely that the man is covering up his "shortcomings." In the next few pages, I hope to clear up some of the misconceptions of penis size and assure you that if you are dissatisfied with your penis size, you can take specific steps to change it.

Dr. Alex Comfort, the eminent sexual researcher, emphasizes the importance that a man places on the size of his penis. In his list of causes of

---

❏   The term "buggery" comes from the fact that early Bulgarians had a low birth rate and were accused of practicing anal intercourse.

sexual problems in men, concern over penis size sits right at the top. And this is not just a Western phenomenon. Cultures worldwide esteem the large phallus. Tribal shamans in the Ivory Coast have fully exploited this preoccupation with penis size. Their most effective weapon against enemies and unruly tourists is to threaten them with a curse to reduce the size of their penises. *Men's Health* magazine recently reported an amusing anecdote of this curse in action. When the local police came across a band of Nigerian fisherman preparing to lynch witch doctor Ibrahim Hassane, the authorities wanted to know why. The fishermen explained that the shaman had placed a curse on them which reduced the size of their penises by two-thirds. One by one, they showed their diminished genitals as proof. The accused witch doctor confessed to his mischief but refused to provide the details of his magic (I wonder if he has a curse that does just the opposite?).

The advantages of a large penis

A large-sized penis has a number of distinct advantages over a small-sized organ. Not only is a large penis a source of immense pride and satisfaction to its owner, it also instills desire and awe in his sexual partner. The size of the penis also plays a great role in providing physical and sensual pleasure to the partner. A large, thick penis has the capability of stretching the vaginal (or anal) muscles to a much greater extent, and provides the partner with a sense of being completely filled and totally penetrated. Also, the actual length of the intercourse stroke plays a large role in the sexual sensation that can be enjoyed by both partners.

Let's clarify a very important point here. A large penis by itself amounts to little if the owner is an absolute oaf who is devoid of sexual adroitness and alacrity. Technique and attention to a lover's needs are by far the most important function in determining sexual satisfaction. Most penises and vaginas (and other willing orifices) fit together remarkably well, and a deficit in a man's size can SOMETIMES be compensated by technique. I emphasize the word "sometimes" simply because the sexual organs of men and women all vary in size. Contrary to popular belief, not all women are created equal. Some have narrow and shallow vaginas while others are dilated and deep. Even a tight vagina can stretch to accommodate a huge

---

❏   In 1415, the original Pope John XXIII was deposed for "notorious incest, adultery, defilement, homicide, and atheism." Earlier when promoted to cardinal in Bologna, "200 maids, matrons, and widows, including a few nuns fell victim to his brutal lust."

penis (after all, it is built to permit the passage of a baby). However, a woman with a spacious vagina will not feel much sexual pleasure with a man possessing a finger-sized penis. Let me provide a couple of examples.

This stupendous Scandinavian phallus measures 9" long when flaccid (23 cm) and increases to an unbelievable 11" (28 cm) when erect. This size is found in perhaps 1 in 100,000 men.

Steve, a reader of my newsletter, *Penis Power Quarterly* wrote to tell me his story. He is a man with an incredible-sized penis as thick as a man's wrist (over 8" around). Because of his unique--ahem--talents, he has employed himself as an "escort" to some of the nation's most powerful women. For a three figure fee, he services women who seek to be fully penetrated with his horse-sized organ. He comments how each woman is built differently, and frankly, a few have been unable to accommodate him. Amazingly, the woman with the deepest and most commodious vagina was a never-married, middle-aged female.

Rob, another *Penis Power Quarterly* subscriber, wrote to tell me that he planned to undergo surgical enlargement to increase the girth of his organ. He explained that he was getting married to a woman with a

❑ In the early 1700's, homosexuality was widespread through England. In a letter to a friend, Elizabeth, Duchess of Orleans, wrote that "nothing is more ordinary in England than this unnatural vice."

capacious vagina whose first husband was very well-endowed. He wanted to be sure that he could provide the same measure of pleasure as hubby #1.

For every woman with a large vagina there exists a counterpart with a small orifice that would be uncomfortable with a large penis. In *The Tao of Sexology,* Stephen T. Chang M.D., asserts that the anatomical fit of the man's organ with his partner's orifice is the most important consideration.

> The size of the penis is important for only two reasons: 1) the psychological effect on the man who happens to think his penis is too small, and 2) its compatibility with the size of his partner's vagina. It is more important that the penis be compatible with its counterpart.

Apart from technique, what really matters to women is thickness. The thicker the penis, the greater its potential for stretching the walls of the vagina to provide that feeling of complete penetration. Even gay men who engage in anal intercourse often agree that the thicker penis provides greater sensation (and a pleasurable challenge).

Interestingly, when men offer their measurements (five inches, seven and a half inches, etc) they are referring only to the length. Thickness is but a minor consideration. To men, length is what matters. It is the numbers game by which men compare themselves to others. On the other hand, if women were doing the measuring, the important statistic would be girth.

Technique vs. size

We have been force-fed the notion that technique is much more important than size. My criticism is that there is a great deal more to this issue, and the experts for the most part, have chosen to leave it untold. Actually, technique AND size should be considered with equal importance. The average person would agree that lovemaking technique, rather than size by itself is more important. Given the choice between a clumsy maladroit buffoon with a 9" (22 cm) penis and a suave, handsome, charismatic tycoon with a 5" (12 cm) peanut, most of us would opt for the latter. But instead of stacking the deck, let's say the choice lies between two men identical in attractiveness, mannerisms, and sexual technique. The choice would obviously go to the man with the larger penis (unless, of course, the partner cannot comfortably

---

❏ The Empress Catherine the Great of Russia hand picked the most well-endowed men from her ready stable of handsome Imperial Guards to be her lovers. Each went through a physical examination and was often required to "audition" to prove his size, talent, and durability.

accommodate a large penis). This is the specific type of question that sex researchers should ask, but are quite reluctant, for fear that the preference for the larger penis would dispel their theory of superior technique.

Vernon Bosch states that all men are better served by knowing the truth about genital size:

> What is the neurotic impact of the revelation that, in some cases, a penis may be too small? Does it shatter his ego or make him into a sexual cripple? Do the facts of the matter serve to enlarge his anxiety? Or, as we have suggested, does the truth lessen anxiety? Isn't fore-warned fore-armed? And isn't it infinitely better to learn the facts of genital disproportion from, say, this book--than from a surprising and possibly traumatic experience?

To illustrate the advantages of a large penis, let's first cover a few facts relevant to the female anatomy. While the vagina may be limited to a depth of 7" (18 cm) or so when sexually stimulated, a man with a 7" (18 cm) penis will only be able to effect a 6" (15 cm) penetration (or much less if he is overweight). Similarly, a man with an 8" (20.5 cm) organ might achieve a 7" (18 cm) penetration. Dr. Stiller, in *Sex Organ Size* theorizes that many women achieve orgasm by rhythmic pressure on the cervix. A short penis (less than 6") would obviously have difficulty reaching the cervix. A thicker penis also applies more pressure to the area below the clitoris by stretching the vaginal opening. In his *Ideal Marriage* written back in 1930, Thomas Van de Velde, MD, wrote that:

> On the whole, a phallus of unusual size must be more agreeable to women on account of increased pressure and friction in coitus. If a small penis is matched to a large vagina, the sufferer will be the woman.

In our society, we always seem to place the blame on the woman. "She's too loose," "She's too big," "She's not tight enough" are the complaints often heard in the locker room. It's time that men share responsibility in sexual matters. For their own sanity, modestly-endowed men should learn to accept their smaller status with humor and aplomb. This admission should in no way diminish their sense of masculinity and self worth, for the penis in all its various sizes and shapes is a marvelous and beautiful creation. Also, a modest-sized penis is of much greater utility to a woman with a shallow or narrow vagina. However, if an underhung man is

---

❏   "A man sleeps an average of two to three hours a night in full erection," says Irwin Goldstein, M.D., co director of the New England Male Reproductive Center at Boston University.

uncomfortable with his status, he can search out methods of penis enlargement (manual or surgical) or learn more effective ways to please his partner.

What women think about penis size

Is penis size important to women? Sex therapists tell us that technique, rather than size, is what matters most. However, recent studies show that many women perceive the larger penis to be more powerful and more sexually-stimulating. Psychologist Judy Kuriansky PhD agrees with this assessment, telling her listeners that "surveys show that up to half of all women believe a man's sexual size matters, associating size with power, prowess, or pleasure." Another prominent researcher commented:

> Many females find a small penis to be less psychologically arousing during foreplay than an average or large penis...which symbolizes aggressivity, power, strength, and masculinity. Also, where the penis is larger than normal, the woman may find the prospect of intercourse more exciting and thereby achieve higher levels of sexual arousal.

Years ago, an interesting letter was submitted to *Playboy* magazine by a reader who had conducted her own survey. Among the women aged 25-50 who had borne at least one child, not one was found in favor of a small penis. Of course, such a cursory survey is scientifically worthless, but it does point out that a few women are willing to voice their preference for a larger penis. Dr. Dick Richards argues that size indeed does matter to women.

> The arguments of women who say that it is performance rather than size that matters most are irrelevant to men. We are not talking about a totally logical situation. Nothing will ever convince the average man that big is not best. Size does matter and within limits it quite certainly does matter immensely to women too. The comment of the experienced woman is usually that although other things like skill and care for their feelings matter a great deal, when all other things are equal, the larger penis is the more appreciated. And there, in a nutshell, is the significant factor of all the prolonged discussions on the relevance of penis size. The majority of women answer the same thing,...better a good big one than a good little one. Men and women alike, for their different reasons, prefer a big penis to a small one.

❑   In his book, *Sex over 40,* Saul Rosenthal cites a survey that found that 2/3 of men in their 50s masturbate at various times.

In the August 1989 edition of *Players* magazine, writer Donna Powell cites an informal study in which fifty females ranging in age from 18-45 were asked which penis size they would ideally select for their partner. Four sizes were listed--small, medium, good-sized, and large. 47 of the women placed an "X" next to "good-sized" whereas three women opted for "medium." In another clinical study, 36 male and 24 female college students were shown slides of a large penis and a small penis and asked to describe their psychological reactions. The large penis was characterized as "stronger," "more active," and "more virile" than the smaller organ. Dudley Seth Danoff, M.D., disavows the fact that size matters to women.

> In my 20 years of practice, I have never had a female come to me and ask me to make her man's penis larger or fatter or wider, but I have often been asked to make it firmer and make it attached to a nicer, more pleasant fellow.

Pioneer sex researcher Virginia Johnson-Masters disagrees. In an interview, she commented on women and penis size: "If a female believes that a large penis is the most exciting and stimulating thing for her, then it is." Publicly, most women will state that technique, rather than penis size, is the more important attribute. But privately, many women state otherwise. In a poll conducted by *Glamour* magazine, a majority of the women surveyed rated medium- to large-sized penises as the most desirable. Years earlier, Kinsey research concluded that women don't have a preference for larger penises over average-sized ones. This is likely due to the fact that most women don't achieve orgasm through vaginal penetration alone. Psychotherapist Joy Davidson, Ph.D. says

> It's not so much a question of size but how a man and woman fit together. It has to do with the placement of the clitoris, the lovemaking position or just how physically compatible a couples' bodies are--if they are different heights, different shapes.

Penises can be long, short, thick, or thin. Vaginas, on the same hand can be wide, narrow, deep, and shallow. Multiplying the possibilities, the odds against locating a partner with a perfect fit for your organ is something like 1 in 16, according to the experts.

❏   Kinsey sex researchers found from their research that 3 of 4 men reached orgasm within 2 minutes of starting intercourse.

The vagina does tend to stretch and dilate after several years of marriage and especially following the birth of children--all the more argument in favor of a large penis. A joke that has been making the rounds tells of a couple that has been married 25 years. The wife is trying to convince her husband that they should go on a second honeymoon. Finally, he relents and says: "Okay, but this time, it will be ME who hangs on the bedpost and screams 'it's too big, it's too big!'"

Popular literature abounds with images of huge penises. In Nancy Friday's seminal study, *My Secret Garden, Women's Sexual Fantasies,* a large percentage of women fantasize about being seduced and penetrated by men with foot-long penises. Clarissa, one of her research subjects admits: "I imagine I am being loved by a fertility figure with an enormous penis far out of proportion to his body. It has nothing to do with being dissatisfied with my husband's penis, I just seem to imagine that this enormous, long, thick, penis (with a giant knob on the end) is entering me." Another subject, Annabel relates her fantasies: "Some of the sizes of the men in my fantasies are nine and twelve inches. And as I have to open my legs wide to take them, the erotic pleasure I have always brings on the most wonderful orgasm."

One of my female readers recently wrote concerning her predilection for the well-endowed male:

> Your books are written from a male viewpoint and seem to express the theory that women are turned off by well-hung males. From the women's viewpoint, sex is better with well-hung males, and we know it from experience. We women enjoy seeing a bulging male crotch and dreaming about what it contains.

Dr. Dick Richards sums up the powerful erotic sensations that the sight of a large penis can instill in a woman.

> A woman will usually prefer the sight and feel of a good substantial penis. She will feel more influenced by it. She will feel prouder to have its care and attentions. She will have a sensation of pride and achievement that she has been integral in making that penis swell up to its full sexual stature. He, for his part, feels able to show his penis off without chance of ridicule and indeed, with his own feelings of pride. There is no doubt that whatever its actual ability, a fine, proud, turgid penis usually wins over a spindly, floppy, small one.

❑   The United States is the only country that routinely circumcises its male infants for non-religious reasons.

32

Most women have never experienced sex with a truly large penis and claim that size is of no importance. However, many change their minds after trying a larger organ on for size. This fact was borne out by a clinical study conducted in the U.K. a few years ago. A physician set out to test the effectiveness of an experimental penis enlargement regimen on a group of participants (we'll discuss this in chapter 7). Before the clinical trials began, the spouses of the men in the study were asked various questions regarding their partners' participation in a penis enlargement study. Predictably, 87% of the women were indifferent, stating that the size of her partner's penis was of little consequence. Amusingly, at the end of the trial (in which 28 of the 32 participants had experienced a verifiable increase in penis size), 67% of these women had changed their minds, stating that the larger penis had truly benefited them--not only because of the more pleasurable sensations that it provided both partners, but also because of the increased confidence and pride that the larger penis instilled in its owner. A swing of -87% to +67% in the space of a four month period is indeed statistically noteworthy.

Whatever the source of a man's obsession with the size of his cock, mankind everywhere associates the penis with dominance. Notice how adolescent boys often play "Let's see who's got the biggest one" at Boy Scout campouts and teen slumber parties. Although men outgrow the ostentatious displays of phallic dominance found in juvenile games, this innate sense of curiosity carries over into adulthood. Most men would never admit it, but discreet comparisons DO take place, even among heterosexual men to see how the guy at the next urinal or adjoining shower is fixed.

Even if a man ventures a glance at the cock next to him, such a gesture is usually casual, innocuous, and seldom sexual in intent. Rather, most men are merely interested in making a quick comparison to reassure themselves that they, too, are adequately endowed. Such comparisons are merely a reflection of the competitive nature of men--the same reason why they seek to impress others with a spacious house, a luxurious automobile, or a hefty bank account. Big muscular men are presented as our superheroes. Big wide cars and expansive mansions are great status symbols. Big diamonds and precious gems all speak of wealth. Big breasts exude sexuality. Big. Big. Big. It would indeed be unusual if there were any appeal at all in the small penis.

❑   In the biblical book of Enoch, we read that the world's first two-legged creatures (whoever they were) had massive penises.

Now please answer the following question in complete honesty. Regardless of the size of your penis, would you take another inch if the "cock fairy" could magically grant such a wish? 95% of you undoubtedly answered "of course." I suspect that the remaining 5% are either great liars or already hung like Missouri mules!

To summarize, a large penis has an inherent number of advantages, including:

❑   Pride of ownership. Without a doubt, both sexes view a large cock with a great deal of respect and admiration.

❑   Enhanced appearance and masculinity. A large, well-developed penis goes a long way toward enhancing a man's sense of virility, dominance, and healthy ego.

❑   Greater sexual flexibility. Anatomically, a large penis is better-equipped for a variety of sexual positions and is uniquely capable of providing deep penetration.

❑   Greater stretching potential. A thick penis is more capable of fully stretching the sphincter muscles of the vagina and anus to provide greater sexual stimulation.

❑   Greater sensation. The larger the penis, the greater the surface area. And as it is the surface area which receives the external stimulus, then clearly, the greater the size of the penis, the more sensation it can receive.

Like it or not, bigness is important to most men (and many women). This is a fundamental sociological fact of life which shall not disappear any time soon. Take a look at our contemporary he-men--Arnold Schwarzeneggar, Bo Jackson, and Joe Montana. They are all big men. Now compare them to Woody Allen, Dudley Moore, and Danny DeVito. Despite their intelligence and contribution to the arts, do they instill the same feelings of masculinity, virility, dominance, and raw, unbridled sexuality? Hardly.

Perhaps the most cogent comment on penis size comes from author Mark Strage. In *The Durable Fig Leaf,* he comments: "Perhaps after all has been said and properly analyzed, it may just be that the size of his penis IS something for a sensible man to worry about."

❑   Certain Native American tribes are known to stage competitions for the largest and ugliest penis.

34

3

How big is big?

The size of a man's penis really depends upon who's doing the measuring, and where he's measuring from. The personal ads in male-oriented publications are inundated with pseudo-studs claiming 8", 9", and even 10" cocks. "Models" and "Masseurs" (usually euphemisms for hustlers) are particularly guilty of phallic bombast--their measurements are almost always exaggerated by an inch or two.

If you were to conduct a Masters & Johnson-type interview and ask 100 men to reveal their penis size, 99 of them would likely exaggerate their measurements. A few of these men probably have never measured their penises and are only providing estimates (on the high side, of course). Others probably don't know how to accurately measure themselves. A more logical explanation, however, is that no man wants to face up to the fact that he is "less of a man" than the next guy. Besides, if no one's going to call his bluff, the man has nothing to lose by padding his measurements. A friend of mine tells me that at cat shows, the length of the feline's tail is measured from the anus to the tip of the tail. Apparently, most men measure themselves this way as well.

❑   An item in *New Scientist* reports on a Cairo University researcher's claim that men in his 18-month study who wore 100% polyester underwear had significantly fewer erections that those who wore cotton.

In a recent Kinsey report about American sexual habits, the researchers asked both men and women to estimate the length of the average adult penis in its erect state. Most of the male respondents answered "eight to twelve inches," whereas the average woman answered "less than four inches."

Why do men grossly overestimate the size of the erect penis (as in the Kinsey study)? Simply put, men think they should measure up to what are basically products of fantasy. Most heterosexual men have never seen another erect adult penis in the flesh. His comparisons are largely relegated to the locker room--where he only sees flaccid organs--and to pornographic videos in which the actors are selected on the basis of their enormous erections. When men see how the actresses react with orgasmic passion toward these humongous penises, they assume that women will only respond positively to an oversized organ.

The lionization of the large penis is perpetuated in popular literature. *The Betsey* by Harold Robbins and *The Godfather* by Mario Puzo contain scenes in which the female characters lust for huge penises. These same women complain that their romantic pursuits bring them in contact with underendowed men.

When a man receives subliminal messages that a large penis is vital to his partner's sexual satisfaction, he is bound to develop an image of phallic inferiority. No wonder most men feel small. Unfortunately, as Bernie Zilbergeld, Ph.D., remarks, "the real always loses when compared to the creations of human imagination." Indeed, truly large penises (over 8" in length) DO exist, but as we will see in the next few pages, they are statistically rare.

Believe me, if all men truly possessed large penises, we would do away with a great deal of the impotence, anxiety, and sexual frustration so prevalent among the men of the world today. Who knows...naively, we might even bring an end to internecine wars and global strife. After all, what do men fight for...power, dominance and prestige--all of the symbols inherently possessed by a large penis.

A super-secret research project allegedly conducted by the Pentagon concluded that men with the smallest penises make the fiercest soldiers. This seems to make sense, for isn't aggression merely a capricious and juvenile

---

❑   The human penis is huge in comparison with that of the gorilla, which seldom exceeds 3 cm. (1 1/2") when erect.

tool which men employ to establish their dominance over one another? It is rumored that Hitler was greatly disturbed over his modest endowment, and it is an established fact that the original megalomaniac, Napoleon, suffered from a hormonal deficiency which resulted in a puny, atrophied penis. This possibly contributed to his aggression and frustration. Alas, poor Josephine! What man WOULDN'T be angry at the world?

The correct method of penis measurement

So, how do you go about measuring the honest and correct size of your penis? Believe it or not, there is a medically-mandated method that urologists use to fit their impotent patients for a penile implant. Precise measurements are critical--a half inch variance in the size of the prosthesis can be disastrous. The medically-correct method is to place a ruler firmly against the pubic bone on the top side of the erect penis and measure to the distal end (tip) of the glans. Researchers William A. Schonfeld and Gilbert W. Beebe specify the correct method of measuring the penis as "the linear distance along the dorsal (top) side of the erect penis extending from the *mons veneris* to the tip of the glans." Measuring from underneath is NOT the correct way. You can even measure the erect size of your penis WITHOUT an erection. How? By simply stretching the flaccid organ out as far as it will go. This approximates the measurement of the erect penis. Later, we'll prove that the stretched flaccid length very closely approximates the erect length with a mathematical formula.

Porn stars are celebrated examples of phallic hyperbole. The late John Holmes was particularly guilty of inflating his dimensions. Porno marketers took liberties by touting him as "the foot long stallion" and the "13 inch schlong." While he may have been the crown prince of porno cocks, he simply didn't approach these measurements. After all, did you ever see him hold up a ruler to his erection to verify the allegations? No. The truth is that John Holmes measured a hair short of 10"--which is incredible in its own right. Here's how I know his true measurement. A friend of mine in San Francisco, Bob, sports one of the largest organs in the city. He tells me that 15 years ago, he ran into John Holmes. In the privacy of a hotel room, they compared endowments and were surprised to see that their erections were

❏ In humans, the number of sperm cells released in a single ejaculation is 175,000 times more than the number of eggs a woman will produce in her entire lifetime.

nearly identical in size, shape, and thickness. I recently measured Bob's erection. It topped the ruler at 9 3/4". Incidentally, my forearm (from elbow crease to wrist) also measures 9 3/4". You can use your forearm as a rough guide when someone claims to sport a 10-incher. Unless his erect penis is as long as your forearm, you know that he has stretched his measurements.

The world's dozen largest penises--are you ready?

Now for the pièce de résistance. How big is the biggest one? Since this book is about the penis, and ostensibly about the big penis, I think the answer might interest you. When Dr. David Ruben's revolutionary book, *Everything you've always wanted to know about sex, but were afraid to ask* first appeared in 1970, the section on penis size was the subject that most readers immediately turned to. As a precocious pubescent lad, I remember crouching in the aisle of a department store's book section, furtively glancing at a copy of the hardback edition the month it came off the press. I wanted to know how large I could expect my penis to be when I reached adulthood. But more urgently, I wanted to know who had the biggest cock and how large it was.

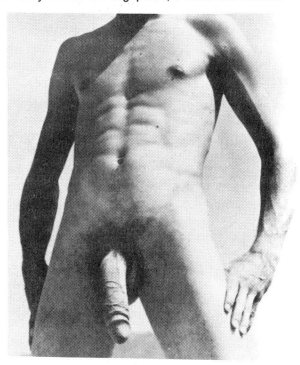

The late porn star John Holmes measured 9 3/4" (22.5 cm) when erect--a phenomenal size, but far short of the foot-long allegations.

❏   A recent survey of men conducted by *Details* magazine showed that 39% of the respondents thought their penis was too small.

Hang onto your hats. My research has uncovered a dozen men who require a yardstick to measure their penises! Let's find out who these cock champs are and where they can be found.

1) Dr. Ruben states that the largest erect organ ever measured topped the rulers at around 14" (35 cm). The proud owner allegedly lives somewhere in Indiana.

2) Several decades ago, a researcher known only as Dr. Charpy conducted research into the size of the adult penis (alas, I was too young to be his research assistant) and records the largest one he found at 13 3/4" (35 cm).

3) Dr. Frederick Rossiter states that there is a medical record (further details are not provided) of a man who measured an incredible 18" (45 cm).

4) Rumors have been circulating for 50 years about the legendary endowment of gangster John Dillinger. While alive, he became somewhat of a romantic folk hero among women who lusted after his power, mystique, and incredible penis that was allegedly as long as his shotgun. An attending physician at his autopsy claimed that Dillinger was endowed about as well as other men. However, several credible sources suggest otherwise. A friend of mine who is a movie producer once did a feature on Dillinger. Following on reports of his endowment, he sent an associate producer to Washington where the severed phallus of the gangster lies in a bottle of formaldehyde in a back room at the Smithsonian Institute. One other source also claims to have seen the foot-long phallus there as well. Indeed, the Smithsonian receives over 100 written requests a year to see it. I have yet to verify this story. What sounds strangely suspicious is that 1) someone would be given the permission to amputate his penis, and 2) that it would be deemed worthy of consideration for display (albeit in a back room) at the Smithsonian. If you have further proof, please let me know.

5) Law professor Anita Hill nearly brought down Supreme Court nominee Clarence Thomas with the mention of the name Long Dong Silver--a black Jamaican man who appeared in a couple of porno loops back in the 70s, including *Seka's Sex Freak Circus.* These loops were subsequently re-released following the Thomas hearings. His penis is truly an aberration of nature which can be tied in a knot with plenty left over to play with. Although the distributors claim his penis measures 18" (45 cm). 15" (38 cm) is more realistic.

❑ A recent magazine survey of over 1,000 men found that "all male respondents, with the exception of the most extraordinarily well-endowed, expressed doubts about their own sexuality based on their penile size."

6) Another legendary megaphallus who appeared in a porno loop is "The Texas Longhorn." In his video he takes his outlandish 14" (35 cm) appendage (whose cockhead slaps against his knee) and deftly wraps it around the neck of an underwhelmed vixen who doesn't quite seem to know what to do with it.

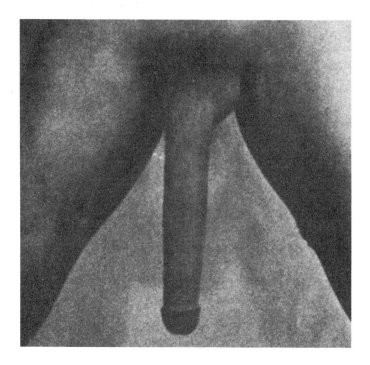

The "Texas Longhorn"

7) A famous German photo of a Massai warrior appeared in *Inches'* magazine a few years back. The warrior appears with his pythonic penis tied in a knot. Unraveled, the organ measured greater than 16" (40 cm) long--FLACCID!

8) The now defunct gay rag, *All Man* showed a photo of New Guinea tribesman wearing nothing but a 15" (38 cm) penis held against the abdomen with a waistcord. The tip reaches midway between his navel and nipples.

❑ In 1895, Oscar Wilde was arrested for homosexuality. Journalist W.T. Stead wrote: "If all the persons guilty of Oscar Wilde's offenses were to be clapped into jail, there would be a very surprising exodus from Eton, Harrow, Rugby, and Winchester (England's most famous private schools)."

9) In the spring of 1991, I received a letter from one of my readers--a respected urologist in the Pacific Northwest. He explained that he was part of a group of 6 doctors conducting research at a major university to determine the effectiveness of an injectible male contraceptive (a GnRH agonist). The study solicited volunteers from the university and paid them a nominal fee for their participation. The volunteers were given complete physical examinations including samples of blood, urine, and semen.

One of the volunteers turned out to be a most unusual and fascinating man. A pre-med student, he had a history of an undescended testicle at age 7, at which time the family physician prescribed a series of testosterone injections. Needless to say, the injected hormone not only encouraged the testicle to descend, it also overstimulated this man's virilizing characteristics. At age 23, he stood 6'3" tall at 250 lbs., and sported a penis of monstrous proportions. The physician writes that he was the most hirsute man he had ever met, with "abnormally profuse body hair totally covering his back, buttocks, arms, legs, chest, stomach, and pubic mound." The most impressive feature, though, was his enormous penis. The physician notes that "the flaccid penis is 32 cm in length (12 1/2") and 18 1/2 cm (7 1/4") in circumference." Remember, these are FLACCID measurements!!! Sam (his name) agreed to let the doctor measure his erect organ, which was recorded at 35 cm in length (13 3/4") by 22 cm (8 5/8") in circumference!! Due to the extreme rarity of this size of penis, the doctor decided to submit the case study to a urological journal, and set about to prepare a sketch for the medical illustrator (of which he sent me a copy). Fitting a life-sized replication of his penis and testicles on the paper required a sheet 21" long (53 cm). He mentioned that when he handed the sketch to the medical illustrator, the artist took one look and promptly fell off his chair. There is much more to the story, and the doctor goes into great detail about this patient in *The Art of Auto Fellatio* by Gary Griffin.

10) Another patient of the above doctor actually appeared in the *National Enquirer*-but not for his world-class phallus. This gentleman sported what is likely the world's longest tongue. Indeed a physical aberration, the photo shows his tongue extending to his mid chest. This is incredible in itself, but what the tabloid didn't mention is that his penis measured over 14" (35 cm) in flaccid length. A VERY confidential photo in my personal collection verifies this equine penis. For the entire story, refer to *The Horsemen's Club*.

❏   In 1928, volume one of the German *Bilder-Lexikon der Erotik* (Picture Dictionary of Erotica) was published. It featured descriptions and illustrations of every imaginable act of sex. Used editions now sell for nearly $1000.

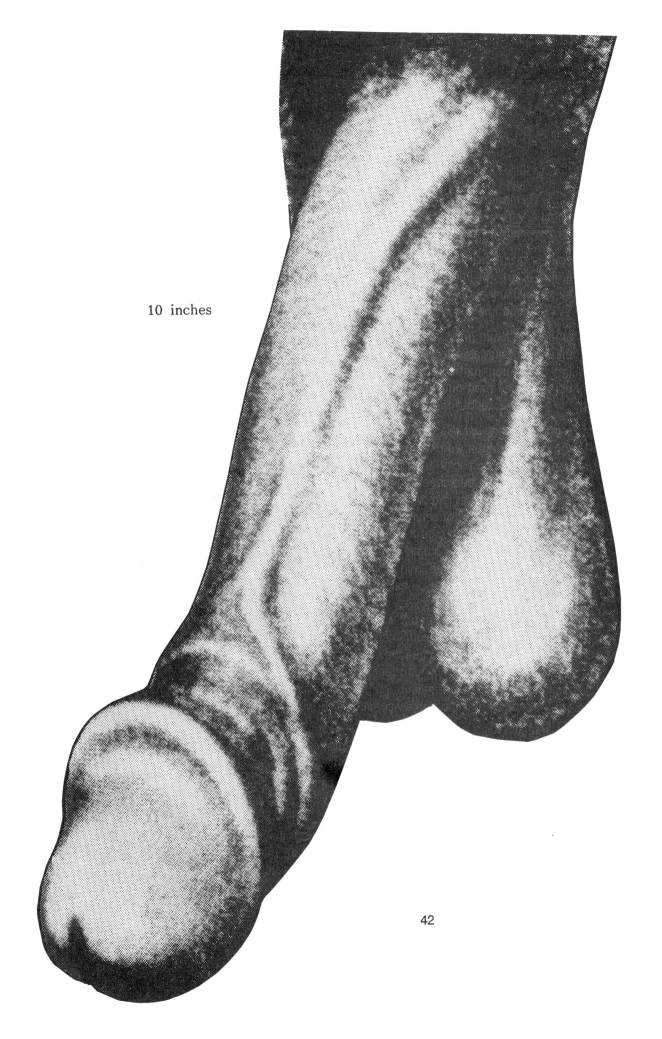

10 inches

42

11) In 1983, I became acquainted with a computer repairman named Dave, who remains elusive and somewhat cloistered to avoid the parade of curiosity seekers who relentlessly follow him once they learn of his endowment status. A tall, slightly overweight man in his late 40s, Dave sports an arm-sized uncircumcised donkey dick 15" x 8" (38 x 20 cm) that can only be characterized as monstrous. It must be seen to be believed. With a simple bend of the head, Dave is able to fellate himself. All of his underwear and trousers are custom-tailored to accommodate the sheer bulk of his elephantine appendage. Several photographs in my private collection verify his status.

12) Several years ago while vacationing in the Mediterranean, I was told to look up a Turkish gentleman by a friend who had met him a few years previously. I wrote an introductory letter and mentioned that I was a researcher interested in the development of the extraordinarily-large male organ. I asked if we might meet over coffee so that I could ask a few questions. He welcomed my visit, and after meeting briefly in a sidewalk bistro, retired to my hotel so that we could continue our highly personal conversation. Sporting a massive frame of 6'8" at 275 lbs., he was built like the Incredible Hulk and had a piledriver to match. A devout Muslim, he explained in fractured English that he had four wives, none of whom could handle him sexually. When I asked him how large he was, he pulled down his white muslin trousers to reveal the most gargantuan specimen of manhood I had ever laid my eyes on. Hands trembling from incipient shock, I fumbled with my briefcase and withdrew a tape measure. His penis, which he managed to bring to a state of erection, measured an unbelievable 14 1/4" (36 cm) in length!! And yes, he was very proud of it. For the rest of the story, refer to *The Horsemen's Club* by Gary Griffin.

These record-breaking cocks notwithstanding, the fact remains that perhaps less than one man in ten million possesses a cock larger than 12" (30 cm) when measured from the top. With this statistical assessment in mind, it is fairly safe to assume that there are probably less than 1,000 men in the world who truly measure longer than 12" (30 cm).

Along this line, I am conducting a unique study into the experiences of extremely well-endowed men whose penises measure over 9" (22 cm). If you fit this profile (or know someone who does) please contact me so that I can send a discreet five page questionnaire which will help complete my study.

❑   A few years ago, a physician addressed a group of mothers-to-be on a TV talkshow. He stated that the bottom opening of the ear (directly above the lobe) provided an indication of the size of the birth canal. He also stated that it indicated penis size. The wider the opening--the larger the penis.

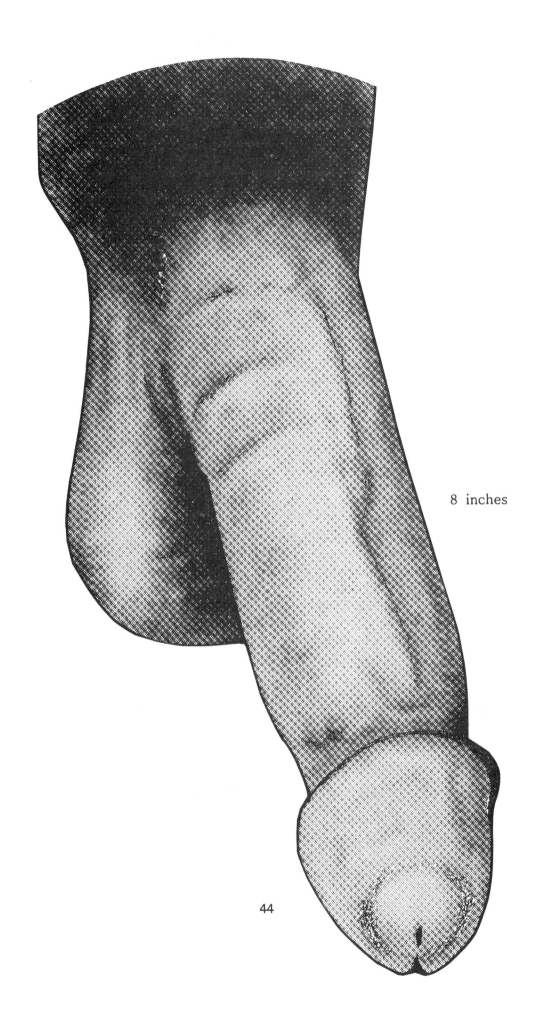

8 inches

44

4

Cock Wars...The Battle of the Races

━━━━━━━━━━━━━━━━━━━━━━━━━

Is there any correlation between race and penis size? Yes and no. Historians of the pre-Civil War South suggest that penis size was a great fear of the whites. Believing that black male slaves might possess penises greater in size than their own, the white masters often feared that once a white woman had experienced sex with a black man, she would never again be satisfied with a white one. A great deal of the sadistic savagery with which the slave trade was conducted stems from this bugaboo. Although slavery has long since been abolished, the horror and apprehension which is associated with miscegenation (racial integration) in America and South Africa is arguably rooted in this fear.

Are blacks really more favorably endowed than whites, or is this merely a mythical assumption that has been perpetuated through the generations? This explosive topic is pregnant with all sorts of sinister ramifications. A few anthropologists have studied this phenomenon but have been greeted with political and professional disdain. A coterie of renegade academicians has even sought to determine the significance of variations between Negroids, Caucasians, and Orientals in respect to IQ measurements and cranial size. Most professionals have decided to leave the topic

❑ In 1972, the English edition of *Cosmopolitan* printed the first male centerfold in its April edition, featuring model Paul de Feu. The American edition, which featured Burt Reynolds on a bearskin rug, immediately sold out, and the number of male purchasers increased dramatically.

45

alone. There is enough racial hatred in our society without kicking up more detritus suggesting the superiority of one race over the other.

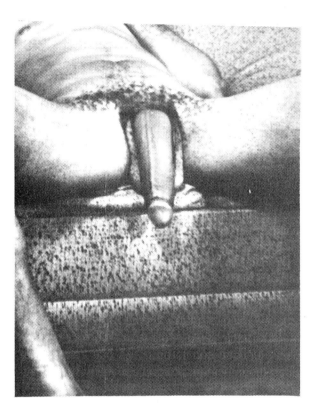

Monstrous black penises such as this help to fuel the myth that all black men are hugely-endowed.

Imagine what the implications would be if it were indeed determined that blacks were better-endowed than whites, who in turn were hung larger than Asians. Would that mean that Asians were on the bottom of the heap simply because they possessed smaller genitals? Considering the fact that they are more prolific (more than a billion of them in China alone) this would hardly seem to be the case. Rather, such a revelation would simply show that one race has larger genitals than the other. Period. Actually, there is enough research available to put the argument to rest once and for all. Let's find out the truth about race and penis size.

Most people tacitly asume that blacks possess larger penises than whites, yet this is only partly true. In the flaccid state, blacks--on the whole--do have an advantage, however, when measured against the erect penises of their white brethren, there is little difference in average length. In *The Penis,* Dr. Dick Richards, MD, comments:

❏   The size of the fully-stretched flaccid penis is the same as the erect penis.

Although it is so that Negroids have larger penises, this is true only in the flaccid condition. At their most powerful erection, they tend in general to lack strength: that is, the degree of distension is less and the rigidity is correspondingly less. It would appear that grounds for this spiteful fear among races are shaky indeed.

From the data that are available on the subject, Caucasians and Negroids possess penises that are comparable in average erect length. The advantage lies in the flaccid state, during which blacks do appear to hang longer. More recent studies show that blacks ARE longer than whites, but only by 1/4" (.5 cm) in average erect length--a difference hardly worth mentioning.

How do other races stack up? Although no scientific studies have been published (to my knowledge) on the subject, enough anecdotal evidence exists to draw educated conclusions.

Considering that Japanese-manufactured condoms measure about an inch (2.5 cm) shorter than their American counterparts, we can safely infer that the erect length of the average adult Asian penis is around 5" (13 cm). An amusing story found in Sidney Biddle Barrow's best-seller, *Mayflower Madam* corroborrates the smaller endowment status of Asian men:

> Several girls actually preferred Japanese clients because they were less demanding sexually. For one thing, they normally took less time in bed. For another, they tended to be (smaller endowed)...Let me sum up it this way: For his monthly column in Esquire, Bob Greene once paid a visit to a New Jersey factory where Trojan contraceptives are manufactured. At one point, Greene tells the plant manager that when he was a teenager, he and his friends used to believe that condoms came in different sizes. As a matter of fact, the manager replied, there really ARE two sizes--one for American men and one for Japanese.
>
> 'What's the difference?' asks Greene
>
> 'The Japanese size is smaller,' the manager replies. 'When you lay one of these goods flat and measure its width, it is fifty two millilmeters wide and seven point one inches long. The Japanese standard is forty nine millimeters wide and six point three inches long.'
>
> From that time on, some of the girls used 'six-point-three' as their private code word for Japanese men.

❑   There is absolutely no relationship between penis size and stature, nose size, hand size, or any other body part. Penis size is purely a matter of genetics and heredity.

47

As further corroborration of the smaller status of Asian men, Thai officials complained that the condoms sent by USAID (United States Aid for International Development) were too large and had to be kept in place with a rubber band.

Native Americans are endowed similarly to Asians. I have corresponded extensively with a reader who has provided fascinating insights into the endowment status of Native Americans. A full-blooded Lakota Sioux, he has worked for the Bureau of Indian Affairs for 30 years. He writes: "I have accumulated over 3,000 records of Indian men that I have observed personally and the average size of their erect cock is 5" long and 5" around."

In the nineteenth century, French Army doctor Louis Jacolliot, who wrote under the pseudonym, Dr. Jacobus X., spent 28 years researching and examining the genitals of primitive peoples around the world. He concluded that the African male possessed the largest penises on Earth, writing:

> In no branch of the human race are the male organs more developed than in the African Negro. I am speaking of the penis and not of the testicles, which are often smaller than those of the majority of Europeans. The genital organ of the male is in proper proportion as regards size, to the dimensions of the female organ. In fact, with the exception of the Arab, who runs him very close in this respect, the Negro of Senegal possesses the largest genital organ of all the races of mankind.

Sir Richard Burton, the legendary English explorer, Orientalist, author, linguist, and translator of *The Arabian Nights,* was also astonished by the megaphalli he encountered among the Sudanese Arabs. He writes:

> There is a great distinction between Arabian and African Arabs, as proven by their penis. The Arabian Arab, being of pure blood, has a very small member. The African Arab on the other hand, is long, thick, and flabby. According to my measurements, the penis of the Arab has an average length when in erection of 7-7 1/2" (18-19 cm) by 1 1/2"-2" (4-5 cm) in diameter, but I have often found a penis measuring 8"-10" (20-25.5 cm) in length by 2-2 1/2" (5-6 cm) in diameter. The organ then becomes a kind of pole...and it would produce serious mischief in the rectum of any poor wretch who consented to suffer its terrible attacks. With such a weapon does the Arab seek anal intercourse...age or sex makes no difference to him.

❏ In Southern Burma, the Peguan tribe inserts tiny gold and silver bells under the skin of the penis. These can be heard tinkling as they walk.

One of the questions I'm often asked is about individual countries and their propensities for larger penises. I hear about the hung Dutch, the massively-endowed Puerto Ricans, the big-dicked Poles, the horse-cocked Yugoslavs among others. The truth is that among Caucasians, there is little, if any difference in collective penis size from country to country. A random sample of 100 adult males taken from each country would not likely demonstrate significant differences.

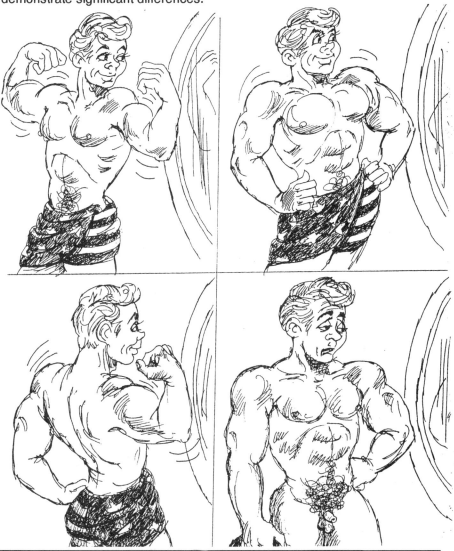

❏   In Ancient Rome, many men engaged in infibulation. The foreskin was pierced on one side while a brass button was sewed to the opposite side. This allowed the man to button his foreskin shut when the penis was not in use.

49

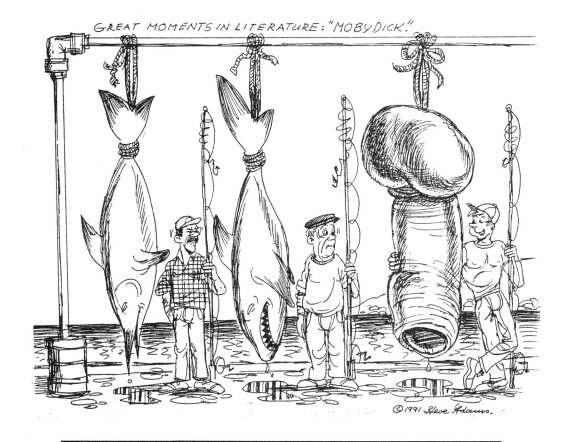

GREAT MOMENTS IN LITERATURE: "MOBY DICK."

©1991 Steve Adams.

❑   A study conducted at the University of Washington School of Medicine measured the penises of 37 full term male infants. The average penile length of these newborns was 3.5 cm. +/- 0.7 cm. and the diameter was 1.1 cm. +/- 0.2 cm.

5

The range of sizes
and penile development

What is the average size of the adult penis? Surprisingly, no one seriously attempted to answer this question until 1949 when noted gynecologist Robert Latou Dickinson began writing his *Atlas of Human Sex Anatomy.* He writes:

> After a vain hunt for such measurements, both here and abroad, I gave carte blanche to the most expert of our library searchers, the late Edward Preble, M.D. He reported that in the long list of volumes consulted 'there is little or nothing to unearth.'

Of the few informal studies that did turn up in the search, Dickinson concluded that the average length of the **flaccid** penis was 4" (10 cm) with an average circumference of 3 3/8" (8.5 cm). The average length of the **erect** penis was 6" (15.5 cm.) with an average circumference of 4 3/8" (11 cm). To bolster his research, Dr. Dickinson conducted a study of his own, measuring the erections of 1,500 males. His study yielded an average erect penile length of 6 1/4" (16 cm) with an average circumference of 4" (10 cm) He also noted that 90% of his sample population measured between 5" and 7 1/2" (12.5 - 19 cm) when erect.

___

❏   At birth, the male infant penis averages 1 - 1 1/2" (5-6 cm).

More recently, a number of independent studies have been conducted to ascertain average penis length. All concur that the absolute average is right around 6" (15 cm). Vernon Bosch, author of *Sexual Dimensions,* states that 90% of all men measure between 4 1/2" and 7 7/8" (11-20 cm) when erect. Statistics regarding flaccid penile dimensions are more elusive, simply because the unerect organ is extremely transitory in size. As any man knows, the penis shrivels up after a dip in a frigid mountain lake, but assumes larger dimensions when exposed to a warmer environment, such as a hot shower or sauna. An analysis of twelve different surveys of phallic dimensions concludes that 90% of all adult males measure between 3.3" (8 cm) and 4.4" (11 cm) when flaccid. This range is very small and suggests that 90% of all men possess penises which are remarkably similar in flaccid size.

The range in size

Penises come in all sizes--small, medium, and large. What is not well understood by most men is the difference between an average vs. a large-sized penis. Many men boast that they are well-hung, but if they knew the truth about penis size, they would discover (probably to their dismay) that they are in fact average. Conversely, many men who think they are small actually fall into the "average" category. The revelation of the truth can have astounding repercussions on a man's psyche. An example of this occurred one day on *The Toni Grant Show.*

Dr. Toni Grant is a well-respected (and beautiful) clinical psychologist who hosted a nationally-broadcasted radio talk show in the 1980s. One day a flummoxed gentleman in his fifties called up and expressed profound anxiety over his inability to achieve a firm erection. Dr. Grant asked him when his erectile problems began. He replied that his erections became limper after his honeymoon. Sensing that something traumatic had occurred during his wedding night 30 years ago, Dr. Grant asked him to relate what happened. He responded that when he removed his shorts for the first time in the presence of his new bride, she glanced down patronizingly at his penis and sarcastically quipped: "Just what do you plan to do with that little thing?"

❏ In Ancient Greece, the Olympic Games were held in the nude. However, it was considered crass and vulgar to expose the glans. To avoid such a phallic solecism, the foreskin was tied shut with a ribbon or piece of string.

That simple derogatory barb emotionally emasculated the man, who was unable to achieve a firm erection from that day on, believing that he was too small to provide pleasure to his wife (whom he later divorced). With grace and aplomb, Dr. Grant asked him how small he was. "Five inches from the top," he responded. "Five inches?" Dr. Grant asked for clarification. "If you're that size, then you're completely normal and certainly in the average category." With that new-found knowledge, the caller's voice suddenly changed. He now sounded completely charged, energetic, and full of vigor. "You mean I'm actually average and not small after all? Well, I can feel it getting firm already!"

Little elaboration needs to be made on the tremendous impact the truth about penis size had on this man's life. Most men have been left in a complete vacuum on how they compare to other men, and the above incident clearly illustrates why it is important to know the truth about penis size.

The ideal penis size

In the 1600s, French surgeon Nicolas Venette wrote a popular sex manual, *Tableau de l'amour Conjugal.* In one of the chapters, he specifies precisely what comprises a big penis, a small penis, and an ideal-sized penis. Wonder if you sport the "ideal" size? Here's what he specifies:

> Nature, which does nothing wihout a plan, established laws for all body parts. Those which serve amorous functions generally have a certain dimension among men and women. The member of the man, according to these laws, should not usually be more than six or eight inches in length, and three or four inches in circumference. That's just the right size which nature has maintained in forming this organ in the majority of cases. If the penis is bigger and thicker, then it takes too much artifice to make it move. For that reason, the inhabitants of Midi (in southern France) are less suited for procreation than we are.

So now we know that the men in the South of France are well-endowed--or at least they were three centuries ago. However, Dr. Venette warns that a large penis can be a hindrance in sexual intercourse. Here's what he has to say about large organs:

❑ In remote reaches of New Guinea and Borneo, several tribes wear nothing but penis sheaths--which can consist of hollowed-out gourds, discarded cans, toothpaste tubes, and even plastic doll arms.

Penises that are too long or too fat are not the best, either for recreation or procreation. They irritate women and signify nothing special. If for no other reason than to make the sex act easier, the man's member should be medium-sized. The thickness of a penis is not as annoying to a woman as excessive length. She has only to enlarge her private parts, which, since they're fleshy and membranous, will easily enlarge as much as one wants. I am not at all speaking here, though of the humongous size of some men's penises. One realizes that these men are not destined for marriage, and one would be very wrong to want the man mentioned by Fabrice of Hilden to remarry, because he had an organ as big and fat as a newborn baby.

Now that we know how one writer felt about penises in the 1600s, let's fast-forward to the present and find out the real distribution of penis sizes.

The distribution of penis sizes

The following graph shows the latest research into the distribution of penis sizes among both black and white college-age males. The graph clarifies several points. First, there is little difference between the size of erect penises of blacks and whites, as mentioned in the previous chapter. Blacks do have a slight edge, but not enough to make more than 1/3" (1 cm) difference in the erect state. Secondly, the graph is highly skewed toward the 6" mark--in fact, 1 of 4 men measures exactly 6" (15 cm). Thirdly, 80% of all men measure between 5" and 7" (13-18 cm). This goes to show that most men are indeed similarly endowed.

With this knowledge, we can infer the following:
❑   A small penis measures less than 5'' (13 cm) when erect
❑   An average-sized penis measures 5'' - 7'' (13-18 cm) when erect
❑   A large penis measures greater than 7'' (18 cm) when erect

The table on page 57, taken from *Sexual Dimensions: The Fact and Fiction of Genital Size,* graphically illustrates the distribution of penis sizes among adult males. Note that the distribution of men from 4" - 9" (10-23 cm) follows a typical bell-shaped curve, meaning that the further one goes from 6" (15 cm)--either up or down--the fewer men there are. In other words, extremely large and small penises are very rare.

❑   When males of the aboriginal Walibri tribe of central Australia greet each other, they grab penises instead of shaking hands.

MEASURED LENGTH OF ERECT PENIS

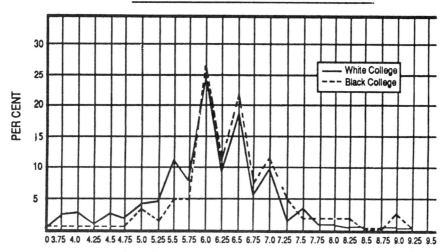

MEASURED LENGTH TO NEAREST ¼ INCH OF WHITE AND BLACK COLLEGE MEN

These two tables illustrate the distribution of penis LENGTH in the adult male. We know that the average erect length is 6" (15 cm), but what about girth? Whereas length seems to be the primary preoccupation of the male, women generally consider thickness to be the greater asset. In the erect state, the penis ranges from 7/8" - 2" (2 - 5 cm) in diameter, with rare cases exceeding these dimensions. The average erect diameter is 1 1/2" (4 cm). The following researchers conducted studies into penis size and reported the following averages in phallic diameters:

❑   LeMon Clark 1 2/5'' (4 cm)

❑   Van De Velde (5 cm)

❑   Stiller 1 2/5'' (4 cm)

❑   Dickinson 1 1/4'' - 1 1/2'' (4 cm)

❑   Davis 1 1/2'' (4 cm)

❑   Chartham 1 11/32'' (4 cm)

These studies conclude that the average diameter of the adult penis lies right around 1 1/2" (4 cm). The greatest diameter that any of these researchers studied was 2 1/2" (6.5 cm). However, there are a few men around that easily exceed this. I know of two men whose organs measure 3"

❑   A 1979 survey of 1,000 gay men showed that while 37% thought that the penis size of their partner was important, virtually all of the respondents perceived their penises as being too small.

55

(7.5 cm) in diameter--a stupendous girth achieved through a diligent regimen of vacuum hyperemiation. We'll learn about that technique in the chapter 7.

I now fall in the 7"+ (18 cm) category. Before enlarging my penis (through methods that we'll discuss later), I measured a respectable 6 1/4" (16 cm), but certainly was not satisfied with being average. If you happen to be one of the lucky individuals who falls in the upper 10% of this table, you may be satisfied with the present size of your penis. However, some men, no matter how large, are still interested in gaining even more length and girth. A married attorney in Missouri sports one of the most impressive penises in the country--an incredible 9 1/2" (24 cm) whopper which draws stares of incredulity at his athletic club, yet he is still performing daily penis exercises in an effort to acquire even greater dimensions. Another man in Vermont tops the ruler at an unbelievable 11" x 8" (28 x 21 cm) when erect (I have photos of these astouding men in my private collection) and still engages in daily vacuum pumping sessions to develop his penis to even greater dimensions --all with the encouragement of his wife.

The Incredible Sears Catalog Caper

Back in the 1970s, the department store giant, Sears-Roebuck published its renowned annual catalog. What slipped past the editor's eyes in one particular issue created such a brouhaha that the catalog quickly became a collector's item.

The underwear section, known for featuring demure and modestly-arranged models, became the object of nationwide attention when it was discovered that one of the male models was so hugely-endowed that his penis actually hung below the bottom hem of the boxer shorts he was modeling. News spread quicker than wildfire, and salacious spinsters, giggling housewives, and curious males snapped up all available copies before the error was discovered by corporate management, who undoubtedly sneaked a few copies for themselves before the rest of the lot was destroyed. The catalog was immediately reshot and replaced by a sanatized, mid-year edition.

❏   Alfred Kinsey demonstrated that 5% of males sport very small penises measuring less than 3.5" (9 cm) when erect. Conversely, a true 9" (23 cm) erection is found in less than 1 in 100 males.

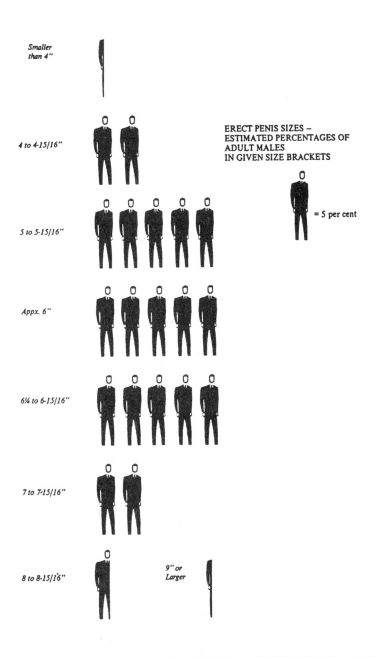

❑   In 14th century Europe, well-endowed aristocrats were permitted to publicly display their genitals. The fashion at the time consisted of tight-fitting
hose that were not joined at the crotch. If the genitals were not sufficiently
large, the man wore a flesh-colored falsie known as a braquette.

In 1993, I began conducting research, mailing out confidential questionnaires to a number of readers asking the following:

❑ What is the length of your flaccid penis?

❑ What is the length of your erect penis?

❑ What is the circumference of your erect penis?

❑ Do you consider your penis to be much smaller, smaller, average, larger, or much larger in size?

❑ Would you like your penis to be shorter, longer, or the same as it is?

❑ Would you like your penis to be thicker, thinner, or the same as it is?

❑ If you could magically change the length of your penis, what size would you LIKE it to be?

❑ If you could magically change the girth of your penis, what size would you LIKE it to be?

To date, 88 of the questionnaires have been returned, providing sufficient numbers to make some observations with a +/-10% confidence rate:

❑ The average flaccid length of the respondent is 4.14'' (10.4 cm)

❑ The average erect length of the respondent is 6.3'' (16 cm)

❑ The average erect circumference of the respondent is 5.5'' (14 cm)

❑ 8 of 88 respondents were satisfied with the current length of their penis

❑ 10 of 88 repondents were satisfied with the current thickness of their penis

❑ 80 of 88 respondents expressed the desire for a longer penis

❑ 78 of 88 respondents expressed the desire for a thicker penis

❑ No respondents wanted a shorter or thinner penis

❑ Of 88 respondents, here is how the men categorized themselves

● 4 = much smaller than average

● 24 = smaller than average

● 36 = average

● 16 = larger than average

● 4 = much larger than average

Again, these results reflect a bell-shaped curve, with nearly equal amounts characterizing their penises as "small," "average," and "large".

❑ Dr. Jacobus, a French surgeon found that the penis and vagina sizes of the various races were closely correlated. In other words, the vaginas of African women are slightly larger whereas the vaginas of Japanese women are smaller to match the phallic sizes of their men.

The most telling results came from the question: "If you could magically change the size of your penis, what size would it be?" When the figures were tallied, the average repondent wished for a penis measuring 9" in length (23 cm) and 7.2" (18 cm) in circumference. This means that the average man wished to be 3" longer (7.5 cm) and 1 3/4" (4 cm) thicker.

Coefficient of expansion

The size of a flaccid penis is an unreliable indicator of the size it will attain when fully erect. Penises that are naturally large seldom increase more than an inch or two during tumescence. The real suprise is found when a man with a small or average-sized penis suddenly becomes a locker room stud upon erection. These men are said to have a large coefficient of expansion.

Several years ago, I had a good friend that I met during my undergraduate school days in Utah. We played racquetball a couple of times and I noticed in the shower that he had a great deal to be modest about. In fact, his penis was so small that it appeared as no more than a pink bud protruding from a thick tuft of pubic hair. I was continually amazed at the steady stream of girlfriends who called on him at all hours of the day (and night). I asked what his secret was, and he replied: "It's all in the equipment." Without stopping to phrase my response with some measure of diplomacy, I quipped "What equipment?" Rather than take umbrage at my comment, he retorted, "Let me show you something." I followed him into his bedroom where he locked the door, retrieved a well-worn copy of *Penthouse,* and with his back to me, proceeded to stimulate himself. Within a couple of minutes, he swung around and said "Take a look." I almost fell off the edge of the bed. This couldn't be the same man. He displayed an enviable, throbbing 7-inch (18 cm) salami that belied its previously lilliputian dimensions. In a near state of shock, I asked him how he did it. He explained that it was no trick--he just happened to have a telescoping cock which kept several coeds smiling on the weekends.

Masters & Johnson conducted several studies into the size variation which occurs between flaccidity and tumescence. They discovered that the smaller penis has a greater coefficient of expansion than the larger penis. In their study, they found that:

❏   Penis Joke: A drill sergeant addresses a soldier who bolts out of bed at reveille: "Private Lewis, why is your penis hanging below your skivvies?" "Because it's cold and it's shrunk up, Sarge!"

40 men whose penises measured 7.5 - 9.0 cm (3'' - 3 3/4'') in length in the flaccid state were compared to a similar number of study subjects whose penises in the flaccid state measured 10.0 - 11.5 cm (4'' - 4 3/4''). The length of the smaller penises increased by an average of 7.5 - 7.8 cm at full erection. This full erection essentially doubled the smaller organs in length over flaccid-size standards. In contrast, the men whose organs were significantly larger in a flaccid state increased by an average of 7.0 - 7.5 cm in the fully erect state.

The researchers reported that the greatest increase occurred in a man whose penis grew from 7.5 cm to 16.5 cm. The smallest gain was in a man who grew from 11 cm to 16.5 cm. In my study, the smallest gain was from 11 cm to 13.5 cm and the largest gain was from 12 cm to 19.5 cm. Masters & Johnson examined 500 men and grouped them into three broad categories:

❑ small penises (2.4'' - 3'' flaccid)

❑ average-sized penises (3'' - 3.5'' flaccid)

❑ large penises (3.5'' - 4.0'' flaccid)

Researchers at the Kinsey Institute conducted a similar study. They measured the flaccid and erect penis lengths of 2,770 men from the base to the tip of the glans. Researchers Paul L. Jamison and Paul H. Gebhard divided the flaccid penises into short (averaging 3.1'') and long (averaging 4.4'') and compared the variation in tumescence. They concluded that the shorter the penis, the more it grew during erection. The penises in the "short" category grew by 85% or more to an average erect length of 5.8'' (14.7 cm). The penises in the "long" group grew only 47% to an average erect length of 6.5'' (16.5 cm). They also discovered that the thinner the penis, the more it widens. The circumference of short penises enlarged by 34% compared to 27% for long penises. The data also demonstrated that height and weight are no predictors of penis size.

Probably the most controversial of Masters & Johnson's findings concerns the fact that homosexuals were found to have larger penises than their heterosexual counterparts. In their words:

One unusual finding concerned homosexuals. The organ of these men was both in length and width, distinctly larger than that of the control group of heterosexual men: 3.3'' (8.5 cm) as against 3.0'' (7.5 cm)...It is difficult to offer an adequate explanation for this finding.

❑ The size of the penis is largely predicated upon the level of testosterone generated in the womb in the first 12-14 weeks of life. If this level is disturbed, the penis will not develop to its full capacity.

Development of the penis--length

We have covered the range of sizes among the adult penis, now let's see how it develops from infancy until adulthood. The following is a compilation of some groundbreaking research conducted by William A. Schonfeld and Gilbert W. Beebe in the 1930s. They set out to determine the normal variation in the size of the developing penis in order to facilitate the diagnosis of endocrine disorders such as hypogonadism and adiposo-genital dystrophy.

A word needs to be mentioned regarding their measurement techniques. As it is clearly difficult to determine the erect measurements of young, growing penises, the researchers used stretched flaccid measurements. This involves the stretching of the flaccid penis and measuring it as if it were erect. As has been mentioned previously, a stretched, flaccid measurement closely approximates an erect measurement. As the size of the flaccid penis can vary greatly according to environmental surroundings, three separate observations were made and the median was recorded.

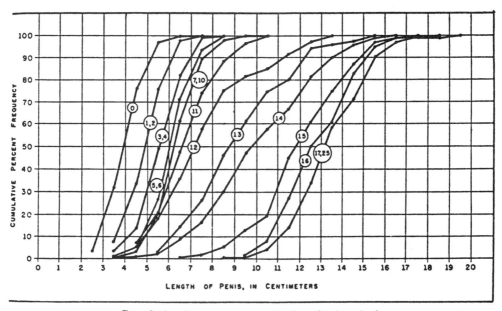

Cumulative frequency curves for length of penis, by age

❏ From birth to age 10, the average penis grows less than an inch--from 1 1/2" (3.5 cm) to 2 1/4" (6 cm). Between age 10 and 16, it generally doubles in size again due to the surge of testosterone in the bloodstream.

In order to determine if the flaccid stretched measurements closely approximated the true erect measurements, the researchers provided each subject with four cardboard strips and instructed them to mark the length of the erect penis on four subsequent mornings. For each subject, the median of the three closest lengths was accepted as the true erect length and was compared to the stretched flaccid lengths. A statistical scatter diagram was constructed which clearly demonstrated that the relation between the stretched flaccid and erect lengths was extremely close. In fact, a line drawn through the points on the scatter diagram was fitted by the method of least squares, resulting in the equation

$$Y = -.0095 + 0.985\,X$$

where Y = erect length and X = stretched flaccid length. In other words, for all intents and purposes Y = X with a correlation coefficient of + .983.

AGE	STRETCHED PENIS				VOLUME OF TESTIS	
	Length		Circumference		First Decile	Ninth Decile
	First decile	Ninth decile	First decile	Ninth decile		
years	cm.	cm.	cm.	cm.	cc.	cc.
Under 1	2.7	5.2	3.1	4.2	.33	.86
1–2	3.6	6.1	3.4	4.5	.59	1.2
3–4	4.1	7.0	3.6	4.6	.61	1.1
5–6	4.7	7.3	3.7	4.7	.59	1.1
7–8	4.9	7.6	3.8	5.0	.60	1.1
9–10	4.9	7.6	3.9	5.1	.68	1.5
11	4.7	8.7	4.1	6.2	.82	5.1
12	4.9	11.3	4.3	7.5	.94	11.1
13	6.1	12.2	4.5	8.3	1.6	
14	6.6	13.5	4.9	8.5	2.0	14.4
15	9.1	14.8	6.1	9.2	5.7	18.3
16	10.8	15.3	6.8	9.3	9.7	
17			6.9	10.0	10.4	21.3
18–19	10.8	15.5	6.9	10.1		
20–25	11.3	15.5	7.2	9.8	10.8	21.5

❏ Growth hormone also plays a crucial role in penis size. Dwarfs who lack sufficient levels of growth hormone (but who have normal levels of testosterone) often have penises that are in proportion with their height.

Development of the penis--circumference

To measure the circumference, the researchers prepared a set of graduated rings measuring 3, 4, 4.5, 5, 6, 7, 8, 9, 10, 12, and 14 cm. The smallest ring that could be comfortably slipped over the stretched flaccid penis was used as the correct circumferential measurement. The subjects were asked to measure their own erect circumferences at home on four successive mornings. A set of square cardboard pieces with round holes was provided to the subject. He was to note the smallest hole that fitted with ease.

Once the researcher had the erect circumferences provided, they were compared with the circumference measurements provided through the stretched flaccid technique. Again, a scatter diagram was devised. Through the aid of a regression equation, valid estimates of the erect circumference was made from the measurements provided from the stretched flaccid penis.

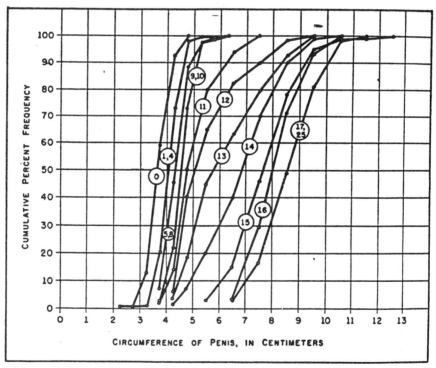

Cumulative frequency curves for circumference of penis, by age

In other words, if you take the measurement of the circumference of your stretched flaccid penis, a simple mathematical equation allows one to determine the size of your penis' circumference when it is erect.

To determine how the penis increases in size as a boy ages, the researchers randomly selected 1,500 white male boys who were patients of medical doctors at 6 different medical clinics in New York City.

The first chart contains 12 separate curves. Each one increases in age from left to right. Here's how to read the chart. The first curve (labeled 0) pertains to the subjects who were less than 1 year old. The numbers at the bottom of the chart refer to the erect length of the penis (in centimeters). Notice how the bottom part of the curve reads 2.5 cm (1"). This means that the smallest penis measured for this age group was 2.5 cm. The top of the curve has the value of 6.5 (2.5"), meaning that the largest erect penis for boys who had not reached their first birthday was 6.5 cm. The left hand side of the chart (the Y axis) is a cumulative percentage of boys who measure a certain length. If we find the point where the first curve intersects the 50%

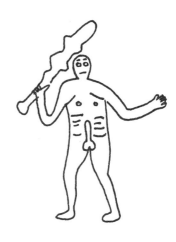

The ancient Cerne giant found in Dorset, England

point on the Y axis, we find that 50% of these boys have erect penises that measure less than 4 cm (1 1/2"), whereas 50% measure greater than 4 cm.

Now let's look at the last curve. Labled 17,25, this curve is a distribution of the erect penis lengths of men aged 17-25. By looking at the bottom and top points of the curve, we can see that their erect penises measure between 8.5 - 19.5 cm (3 1/4" - 7 3/4"). 50% of these men's penises are longer than 13 cm, while 50% are smaller than 13 cm (5 1/8").

The next table shows the numerical values for these ranges. Notice how the greatest increases in penis length and girth occur between the ages

❑   Cuban Jean Baptisto dos Santos was born with two large, fully-functional penises. It is written that he "was possessed of extraordinary animal passion, the sight of a female alone being sufficient to excite him. He used both penises, after finishing with one, continuing with the other."

of 12 and 17--the ages of puberty and adolescence. The final, adult size of the boy's genitals appear to be reached at around age 17.

The following table reads like the first one, but is a graphic depiction of the **circumference** of the boy's penis rather than the length. What is interesting to note is that penis length increases proportionately with other body parts between ages 1-6, but the girth of the penis doesn't begin to increase noticeably until the onset of puberty.

For those who are interested, the table below shows the growth of the volume of the testes from infancy to adulthood. Notice the great variation in the size and volume of the adult testes, which can range from a miniscule 6 cc. to an impressive 33 cc. This chart also shows that very little testicular development occurs before puberty and virtually all boys under age 10 have testicles nearly identical in size.

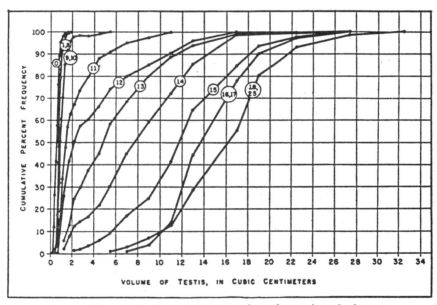

Cumulative frequency curves for volume of testis, by age

❏   18th century Russian nurses believed that they could lengthen the penises of male babies by pulling and stroking the nose.

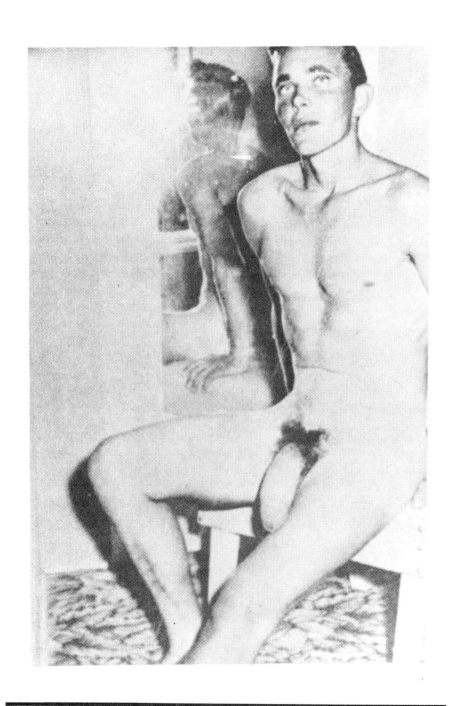

❏   Approximately 1 in 100 males is capable of self-penetration (inserting his penis in his own rectum).

6

Well-endowed celebrities

If you've ever been curious about men in the limelight who are unusually-well endowed, here's the world's most complete source.

I'm often asked how I secured this super-secret information. I have several sources. First, the endowment status of many of these men is well-documented, having been written about by former lovers, spouses, or confidants. Jim Boyd, founder of *The Hung Jury*, the heterosexual dating club for well-endowed men and their female admirers, is another invaluable source. He has collected tantalizing tidbits about the sex lives of well-endowed celebrities for years. Along this same line, Chuck Thompson, a show-biz veteran and friend of numerous stars, has provided fascinating details. He publishes a confidential underground newsletter which recounts the ultra-confidential sexcapades of international celebrities. He also publishes a master list of the circumcision status of over 2,000 men of note. We'll show you how to subscribe to his newsletter at the end of this chapter. But the most fascinating details have come from my readers--many of whom have had "intimate" contact with a specific celebrity and have written to me

---

❏ According to Masters & Johnson, 3 men in 1,000 are able to fellate themselves.

describing their experiences in steamy detail. The ultimate, and most convincing proof, though, are the rare nude photos I have in my collection of such present and past luminaries as Don Johnson, Steve McQueen, Warren Beatty, Victor Mature, Tony Randall, Roddy McDowall, Sylvester Stallone, Burt Lancaster, Aldo Ray, Steve Garvey, and more than 50 others.

With each edition of this book, new information has been submitted by readers like you who have either worked with or have known the particular celebrity and can vouch for his endowment status. In order for a "sighting" to be considered credible, I must receive at least two independent reports from different people. Exact measurements are nearly impossible to come by, so the estimates provided by the viewer must be relied on.

Be aware that celebrities tend to be imbued with a "halo" effect. The fact that they are viewed as larger than life also extends to the genitals. A celebrity's 8" (20 cm) penis (huge by anyone's standards) is almost always perceived by the viewer as much larger. Exaggeration makes the story much more tantalizing. For example, no one would pay any attention to a woman who said, "I went to bed with Frank Sinatra and he had a perfectly wonderful 5-inch penis." More likely, the incident will be related something like this: "Frank Sinatra seduced me with those hypnotic eyes, and we made mad passionate love on the lanai for over three hours, and he had a monstrous foot-long penis." Since viewers almost invariably overestimate the size of a celebrity's penis, we have to view reports of 10", 11" and 12" (25, 27.5, and 30 cm) penises with an extremely jaundiced eye. As mentioned previously, such penises simply do not exist, except, perhaps on larger quadrupeds. According to my research a true 10" (25 cm) penis, measured from the top, belongs to 1 in 10,000 men. A 9" (22.5 cm) penis is found in less than 1 in 100 men. This same statistical distribution also applies to celebrities.

Let's use a quick rule of thumb. I have measured my forearm (from the crease of my elbow to my wrist). This measurement comes to precisely 9 3/4" (24.5 cm). Naturally, then, a 10" (25 cm) penis would be larger than my forearm. Only if a celebrity has an erect penis larger than my forearm will I believe the outlandish claims of 10-12". With one or two exceptions, they probably don't exist. However, let's remember that a true 8" penis is HUGE, possessed by only 2-3 men in 100. This is the cut-off point we will use for this list, so we can say with some degree of confidence that the celebrities who appear in this chapter sport penises that measure 8" (20 cm) or greater.

❑   Here's an anomaly of nature. A four-eyed fish known as Anableps, comes equipped with either a right- or left-handed penis. Understandably, the females also come with right- or left-handed vaginas.

Since the last edition of this book was published, I have received a plethora of new information which has effectively doubled the size of the previous list. I have also removed 5-6 men who have been "revealed" as stars of average dimensions, rather than the gargantuan penises that were previously alleged.

If you have reliable, first-hand information regarding the endowment status of any celebrity (movie star, musician, athlete, politician, author, business tycoon, or other public figure) please write to me directly. These must be first-hand sightings (athletic club, intimate affair, shower, massage, etc.). Provide all the details you can (size, shape, circumcision status, where the sighting occurred, etc.). Of course, your identity will remain confidential. Without further ado, here are those lucky celebrities (in alphabetical order) with cocks to crow about.

Actors

Warren Beatty. Women who have enjoyed Beatty's amorous advances swear that he is hung like a donkey. However, a nude photo in my collection shows that he is average in endowment. In an exclusive interview conducted by *The Advocate* (issue #576) pop icon Madonna was asked how big his dick was. In typical candor, the boy toy responded, "I haven't measured it, but it's a perfectly wonderful size." In her autobiography, *True Britt*, former flame Britt Ekland wrote, "Nature had sculpted him to perfection...without question the quintessential sex symbol." Even sister Shirley MacLaine expressed curiosity, "I'd love to appear in a movie with my little brother one day - and perhaps I shall find out what the fuss is all about."

Ed Begley, Jr. This tall, blond star of TV's *St. Elsewhere* is a recent addition to our list. Several sources have written in, confirming that Begley is indeed one of the hugest in Hollywood, with an erection measuring an honest 10" (25 cm.)

Robby Benson. The former teen idol (born Robert Segal) who starred in *One on One*, *Ode to Billie Joe*, and voice-over in *Beauty and the Beast*, is reported by British gossip journalist Paul Donnelley to sport a cock in the 9" (23 cm) range.

❏ A collection of X-rays of men's pelvises indicated that 75% of men "dress left," meaning that they wear their penises to the left. Tailors have known this for centuries, leaving a bit more fabric on the left side to accommodate the bulge of the genitalia.

Milton Berle. The fact that "Uncle Miltie" is the King Cock of Hollywood is a well-established fact. When he is "roasted" at celebrity events, jokes concerning his mammoth endowment invariably arise. One of the more famous stories involves an incident several years ago when an inebriated man approached Mr. Berle in a bar and wagered that his penis was larger. Milton calmly invited him into the men's room where he pulled out just enough of his penis to win the bet. Although no one has taken specific measurements, it is estimated that his penis measures around 10" (25 cm) when erect. They don't come much bigger than this.

Robert Blackwell. Better known simply as "Mr. Blackwell," this is the gentleman responsible for the notorious "Best-Dressed" and "Worst-Dressed" lists. Those close to Mr. Blackwell are very aware of his huge endowment, which he freely shows to interested parties. A friend of mine was doing Mr. Blackwell's makeup in preparation for a television appearance when he asked if the rumors of his size were true. Blackwell simply unzipped his trousers, removed his massive flaccid organ and said "You be the judge."

Humphrey Bogart. Remembered for his captivating performances in *Casablanca* and *The Caine Mutiny*, this stout and scrawny cinema romantic was reported in Kenneth Anger's *Hollywood Babylon* to lead "the list of the well-endowed." Sources claim that he sported a pendulously-long cock whose only source of satisfaction came from his lifetime love, wife Lauren Bacall. A size 8 (20 cm).

Ward Bond. Star of *Wagon Train*, Bond once allegedly did a public service film for the military which discussed the dangers of venereal disease. He shows how soldiers can "play safely" by wearing condoms. To demonstrate proper condom usage, Bond unrolls a fresh rubber over his impressive 9" erection.

Barry Bostwick. Ask any front row center spectator at Broadway's *The Robber Bridegroom* a few years back. Who cared what the show was about. There was devastatingly-handsome Bostwick in cavalier tights and tunics. As the dancing and show became bigger...so did he. A thick 9" (23 cm), so a few lovers say. Maybe more.

Michael Caine. The popular British actor (born Maurice Micklewhite) is also known to be a talented lover hung in the 8" (20 cm) range.

Phil Carney. A reader reports that the brother of popular actor Art Carney sports one of the largest cocks he has ever seen--reportedly hanging over 8" (20 cm) when flaccid. Could brother Art be similarly endowed?

Keith Carradine. A reader wrote in to offer these observations: "Keith possesses a pendulous 10" (25 cm) cock with a decided downward curve."

Neal Cassady. The hero of Jack Kerouac's *On the road*, this Beat Generation icon was known to be monstrously hung. In Kerouac's book, he describes Cassady's enormous dangle and jokes about his standing in the living room while washing "it" in the bathroom.

Jack Cassidy. The late actor and former husband of Shirley Jones *(The Partridge Family, Oklahoma)*, Cassidy was reported to sport a woman-pleasing sex pole of incredible dimensions. These big dick genes were passed down to sons, Shawn and David Cassidy.

Charlie Chaplin. Whoever coined the moniker "The Little Tramp" never saw Chaplin in the locker room. Jim Boyd writes that "He laid his way through scores of stars, starlets, and teenage nymphs, including leading ladies Edna Purviance, Paulette Goddard, and size queen golddigger Peggy Hopkings Joyce. The latter once asked the comedian over dinner 'Is it true what all the girls say, that you're hung like a horse?' He was indeed, and boasted of his purported 12-incher as 'The Eighth Wonder of the World.' Every bio written about Chaplin reveals him to be a satyr with a passion for teenage girls. This is one case where size was equal to appetite."

Dennis Cole. B-movie actor and ex-hubby of Jacqueline Smith was enjoying a lucrative career until he allegedly got caught up with a Mafia lover, or so the rumor goes. Cole made no secret of his 9" (22 cm.) manhood, often dressing in clingy trousers sans underwear.

Sean Connery. Once voted "the most sexy man in the world," the hirsute and virile James Bond has allegedly bedded some of the planet's most beautiful women. According to Jim Boyd, several of these women report that Connery is both a wonderful lover and "splendidly hung." Before making it big in movies, he posed nude for art classes. One of the students remarked that "the young Sean was magnificent in the nude and certainly lacked nothing 'down there'. In fact, he was the biggest I've ever seen. It made me drop my charcoal pencil."

❏ Does frequent use make the penis larger? In the 17th century, Dr. De Graaf wrote: "Those who go down with any frequency to fight the battles of Venus are always noticing how frequent copulation greatly increases the size of the penis."

Gary Cooper. The star of *High Noon* sported a pendulous penis which was clearly visible under his slacks. Knowledge of his exceptional endowment helped establish Cooper as one of Hollywood's most prodigious lovers. In his biography, a passage describes his affair with Lupe Velez. She is quoted as saying: "He was hung like a horse and could go all night." In Clara Bow's biography, she writes that he "has the biggest cock in Hollywood but no ass to push it around with."

Willem Dafoe. Star of *Mississippi Burning* and *Platoon*, Dafoe is as hung as he is talented. My sources allege that he sports a size 9. During shooting of the steamy movie *Bodies of Evidence*, plenty of Madonna's flesh was revealed, but alas, Dafoe kept his pubic python under wraps.

James Darren. Popular actor and singing star of the early 1960s, Darren (born James Ercolani) had several hit records *(Goodbye Cruel World)* and starred in several films *(Guns of Navaronne)* and TV programs (played Gidget's boyfriend, Moondoggie). One reader writes that Darren was a "well-known, longtime companion to a 50s singing star before he left him and got his big break using his very considerable talent. A HUGE 9" (23 cm), so legend has it."

Ron Ely. Tall, blond, and handsome, the last of the TV Tarzans was also the host of the game show *Name that tune* and the Miss America pageant. Several of my readers allege to have first-hand knowledge of his size, which tops the rulers at over 8" (20 cm).

Eddie Fisher. An Army buddy of his knew him before he married Debbie Reynolds. He was constantly teased in the shower on the size of his "third leg." Fisher was also married to Elizabeth Taylor, who seems to have a penchant for marrying one well-endowed man after another. Jim Boyd writes: "When I spoke with Jane Ellen Wayne....she mentioned that she was working for NBC programming in the 50s when Fisher was a big TV star and that word got around the network that Fisher was well equipped. He would date these women from my office and they would come back the next day or after the weekend and glow over Fisher's sexual capability. They were all talking about how he had either the biggest penis they had ever seen or one of the biggest--and fantastic in bed with it." Ex-wife Zsa Zsa Gabor told Elizabeth Taylor biographer C. David Heymann, "Oh, dahlink, we all knew that Eddie was hung like a horse."

❑ Do you have a long penis? Here are the four longest condom brands sold in the U.S.--Trojan Enz® Large (7 1/2"), Trojans® (7 1/2"), Durex™ Gold (7 1/2") and Maxx® (7 1/4"). Measurements exclude the reservoir tip.

Errol Flynn. The late actor best-known for his salty swashbuckling roles delighted in exhibiting his manhood to close friends. He frequently wore his cock pointing up so that it could be seen emerging from his waistband through his open-to-the-waist ruffled shirts. Truman Capote relates that Flynn pulled out his studly sausage at a party and plunked out *You are my sunshine* on the piano. In his autobiography, *Portrait of a Hollywood Indian.* Iron Eyes Cody writes:

> He was so well-hung that he was famous for it all over Hollywood. In fact, such was his reputation that I know of several perfectly sane directors...who actually asked to see it, right there on the set. Only too happy to settle any lingering doubts as to his masculine dimensions, Errol would unzip and proceed to set the record straight. Regardless of who was present.

Cody also comments on Freddy Frank's legendary endowment, writing that "He and Errol, when the latter was drunk enough--which was most of the time--used to have 'stretch and measure' contests. Always an inch or two short, Errol never conceded defeat, but blamed his drinking--that is, not being sober enough to match Frank's stretching capabilities."

Harrison Ford. A female reader writes that she made it with Harrison back in 1970. She reports that the star of the *Indiana Jones* series, the *Star Wars* trilogy, and *The Fugitive*, is tremendously hung.

Robert Francis. Young star of Columbia pictures' *The Caine Mutiny*, who was killed when his private plane crashed at Burbank Airport. First-handers say Francis' dick was a whopper, measuring nearly 10" (25 cm) and thick.

Freddy Frank. A protegé of Abbott and Costello, Frank occasionally appeared at their private parties, serving salad in a wooden bowl with a hole strategically cut out of the side. Freddy would stick his foot-long "frank" through the hole and pile a mountain of salad on top. With most of the guests tipped off beforehand, Freddy would offer salad to an unsuspecting starlet or self-righteous Bel Air matron. All it took was a couple of scoops with the salad tongs and there would be Freddy's mammoth penis in all its flaccid glory, which never failed to elicit screams of horror from the scooper. Just how big was Freddy Jr.? Rumor has it that Costello once measured it in front of several friends and that it topped the ruler at 13" (32 cm) flaccid! Surely, this is hyperbole and the only ones who know for sure are the scores of

---

❑ If you have a thick penis, the widest condom brands sold in the U.S. are Magnum® (latex), Four Ex® (lambskin), Kiss of Mint™ (latex), and Trojan-Enz® Large (latex).

73

actresses who got banged in dressing rooms between takes. Equally incredible is the fact that Frank was paid for his services out of the movie set's "Miscellaneous Budget." Now you know why we're paying $7 per ticket.

Cary Grant. A former amanuensis of Cary Grant wrote to me, stating that his boss (born Archibald Leach) was a mercurial eccentric who used to teasingly parade around the house in his favorite form-fitting leopard shorts. His flaccid cock lied flat against his belly, almost reaching his navel. A size 8 (20 cm).

Mickey Hargity. Jayne Mansfield's ex-husband, whom she stole from Mae West. A bio of Mansfield reports that she said "Mickey has the biggest cock and I'm not letting go of it."

William Holden. One of my readers writes: "In my celebrity file, I have a shot of Bill with his enormous cock sticking straight out, very thick base with big balls tapering out toward a huge cockhead. Looks to be a good nine inches." No wonder Stephanie Powers misses him.

Rock Hudson. His cock certainly was huge as many can attest. It had a slight curve and measured 8 1/2" when erect (21 cm).

Tab Hunter. One reader writes: "Legendary dick. It is said that one-time lover Anthony Perkins has photographs of adonis Tab sucking his own cock lonnnngggg before it became a cult fave."

John Ireland. Along with Milton Berle, Forrest Tucker, and Freddy Frank, these four were rumored to be the original Alaska Pipeline! Early in his career, Ireland participated in "aqua shows" and his enormous endowment was impossible to conceal, even under modest bathing suits. Casting agents and talent scouts quickly discovered him. When he and his wife Joanne did summer stock together, he was known to put his hand in his trouser pocket and pull the fabric closer to his body to reveal the outline of his flaccid horsecock. The first six rows of those summer sock audiences were known to be occupied by gay size queens who had come to pay homage to their phallic idol.

Sammy Jackson. Former TV star *(No Time for Sergeants)* is currently working as a radio disc jockey in the Los Angeles area. According to a reader of this book, "Jackson's just a simple country boy who says his family never bought him any toys, so he just had to play with his mammoth 9"+ (23 cm) thick, humongous dick."

❏   Male bottlenose dolphins have been spotted masturbating by rubbing the penis on the ocean floor, on the backs of other males, or even on a passing sea turtle.

Don Johnson. One look at the phallus that made *Miami Vice* a prime time staple, and you can see why Melanie Griffiths married him twice. A nude photo (in my collection) snapped of Johnson in his early twenties shows a beercan-thick, uncut penis that would challenge any orifice. Between marriages, Don dated Barbra Streisand, who allegedly refused to consider tying the knot with him unless he agreed to be circumcised. He declined, the relationship ended, and he returned to the welcome embraces of Melanie. His well-publicised drinking binges have landed him in hot water lately. While promoting a Planet Hollywood opening, Johnson slurred words and cursed at radio hosts Ron Bennington and Ron Diaz who requested that he not use the "F word" on their program. "I can do whatever I want," he responded. "I'm rich, I'm famous, and I'm bigger than you."

Van Johnson. One of my readers writes to say that years ago he was cruised in Bloomingdales by the late, great Mr. Johnson. When asked if he went home with him, he remarked, "God no, it was too big!"

Durwood Kirby. Co-host of the original *Candid Camera*, Kirby is known to sport an unusually long penis which dangles half way to his knees.

Lorenzo Lamas. As legendary as his late father, Fernando, so the story goes, and the kid knows how to handle it, or so his many lovers will tell you. Estimates vary, but everyone says it's definitely 8+, which proves his inheritance. Ask mother Arlene Dahl and/or Lamas' widow, star of 1940s swimming movies, Esther Williams.

Michael Landon. One of the all time television legends, the late, great Landon (born Eugene Orowitz) was star of *Bonanza, Little House on the Prairie*, and *Highway to Heaven*. A good friend of mine was a bit-part actor in the '60s who made several appearances on *Bonanza*. He reports that he saw Landon in the shower on several occasions, noting that it was quite long and as thick as a man's wrist.

David Letterman. The popular host of late-night television has been reported to sport an impressive penis in the 9" (22 cm) range.

Ted Levine. The young actor who played the transvestite/killer in *Silence of the Lambs* has a cock 9"+ (23 cm) that is as huge as his talent.

John Loder. One of the most handsome men to grace the big screen, Loder had a brief career, appearing opposite Bette Davis in *Now Voyager*. Tall,

---

❏ The seminal rock band Steely Dan got its name from a dildo described in the William Burrough's novel, *Naked Lunch*.

dapper, and well-educated, he was the son of a British General. Joan Crawford, a notorious size-queen, described Loder as "the most handsome and well-built Englishman I ever met."

Dolph Lundgren. Best-known for his appearances in several *Rocky* movies, tall, blond, buffed Dolph has one of the biggest cocks Hollywood has ever seen. According to members of his Los Angeles health club, Lundgren's cock is in direct proportion to his stature...and they say, too his twin brother doesn't lag far behind. Ask disco legend Grace Jones, who brags to friends she fucked them both--at the same time, saying "He's the biggest I've ever had!"

Dean Martin. The original "Italian Stallion," was described by one high-class call girl as "a very generous man and a terrific lover. He never assumed that because he had a long Italian sausage between his legs that he had it made in bed. He was attentive to my needs and used his big, thick cock like few other men I have known." Comedian Jerry Lewis once made an extemporaneous reference to Dean's cock during a radio promo. Clowning around and trying to outdo each other with compliments, Jerry blurted out on live radio..."and he has a big cock too!"

Steve Martin. This "wild and crazy guy" has no need to be modest in the locker room. Steve allegedly sports a size 8 (20 cm).

Groucho Marx. Take a look at any of the early vaudeville photo pictorials and you're bound to find sepia stills of Groucho and his impressive basket. In a scene from *A Night at the Opera*, he sheds some paper to a certain size, saying "Mine's 12 1/2"." This is obviously a veiled reference to his cock size, although his actual size was probably closer to 9" (23 cm)--still a trophy in anyone's book.

Victor Mature. A popular nude photo taken in the 50s shows Victor lying sideways on a Navy bunk with his pendulous penis hanging over the side. When he was appearing on Broadway in *Lady in the dark*, he boasted, "I not only LOOK like a real stud, I've got the equipment to back it up." The photo certainly backs up his claim.

Tim Matheson. From one observant reader, I received this report. "In Laguna Beach last summer, I ran into Tim, the actor from *Animal House* and many other movies in a restaurant men's room. Imagine my surprise when

---

❑ An Amazonian tribe known as the Mundurucu, refer to sexual intercourse as "eating penises."

76

he hauled out what I would estimate to be 8" (20 cm) soft (compared to my 8" hard). I tried not to be obvious, but it was certainly an eyeful. I would estimate that his cock would be anywhere from 9-10" (22-25 cm) hard."

Roddy McDowall. Famous for his role in the *Planet of the Apes* trilogy, this talented and well-liked actor brandishes an unusually-thick and well-developed organ. A nude photo in my private collection shows a youthful Roddy sporting an impressive wrist-thick, veiny appendage.

Gardner McKay. Heartstopping star of *Adventures in Paradise*--which is exactly how his various lovers described his cock--a huge 10-incher (25 cm).

Steve McQueen. A sexy bear-rug photo (in my collection) taken of the star of *Bullitt* and *The Great Escape* in his early days verifies the description provided by one of his lovers--"Like two Coors beer cans welded together."

Matthew Modine. In the movie *Short Cuts*, he was scheduled to appear nude, but director Robert Altman changed his mind. In the November 5, 1993 issue of *Entertainment Weekly*, Modine comments: "I wanted to come out in the nude in a hot-tub scene, and I was ready to do it, but Altman said that it just didn't seem right. I would have been proud to do it. Look at my hands, look at my feet. They're gigantic! Everything is in proportion!"

Eddie Murphy. Star of *Beverly Hills Cop*, Murphy is known to be very well hung--probably in the 8-9" (20-22 cm) range.

Jim Nabors. Crooner of schmaltzy tunes and star of *Gomer Pyle*, Nabors needs no documentation. His penis has been seen by many individuals who all concur that he is hung like a Missouri mule, measuring 9-10" (22-25 cm) in erect length.

Liam Neeson. Relatively unknown until nominated as "Best Actor" for his portrayal of Oskar Schindler in 1993's blockbuster *Schindler's List*, his reputation as a truly BIG star is now widely disseminated. The big, charismatic Irishman dated Brooke Shields for a time, but now has tied the knot with actress Natasha Richardson. Hopefully, she was well-dilated for her honeymoon. Actress Dana Delaney made an extemporaneous comment on the three biggest dicks in Hollywood, stating that if Liam Neeson, James Woods, and Ed Begley Jr. were placed in the same room, there wouldn't be room for anyone else. Neeson probably tops the ruler at 10" (25 cm.)

❏ The United States has more statutes governing sexual behavior than all of the European nations combined.

Ed Nelson. Popular star of the old *Peyton Place* series has been reported be several readers to have a 9" (22 cm) cock.

Dennis O'Keefe. Actor in comedy and melodrama roles, the late O'Keefe was allegedly hung in the 9" (22 cm) range.

Walter Pidgeon. One of Hollywood's most notorious womanizers, Mr. Miniver was reputed to have "one of the biggest cocks in Hollywood," a rumor he heartily encouraged.

Don Quine. Young star of TV's *The Virginian*, Quine couldn't quite carry aound the burden of stardom, not to mention his mammoth cock (10", so they say). Today he owns and operates a competitive school for young karate devotees and is writing a screenplay.

Anthony Quinn. If they make a movie of his life, is should be titled *Zorba the Hung*. In her autobiography, *Scarlet O'Hara's Younger Sister*, Evelyn Keyes goes into detail about her romantic trysts with Quinn, stating that "there was simply too much of Tony. Legs and arms too long and miles of male body trying (and succeeding) to invade my limited spaces." Another ex-lover wrote "Tony's cock was at least a foot long, very thick and gorgeous-looking. He let me measure it...and then he fucked my brains out."

Aldo Ray. Star of popular '50s films *God's Little Acre* and *Miss Sadie Thompson*, Aldo became involved in porno flicks in the late 1960s. I have a revealing nude photo in my collection which shows an impressive flaccid uncut member hanging at nearly 8" (20 cm).

Christopher Reeve. In *Film Flubs: Memorable Movie Mistakes*, author Bill Givens states that during the filming of *Superman* in England, film censors noticed Christopher Reeve's huge cock hanging on one side of his costume and then mysteriously shifting to the opposite side in subsequent scenes. His huge endowment was so distracting that Reeve was finally fitted with a swimmer's cup to conceal the obvious bulge.

Cliff Robertson. A letter I received from a reader reveals some intimate details about this talented Hollywood icon: "Three years ago I was on a shoot with Mr. Robertson. We were doing one of his AT&T commercials. My only memory of him that day was his constant primping with the hand mirror, fussing with his hair, etc. Later, when I was relating this story to some of my cronies, they interrupted, 'To hell with the mirror, DID YOU SEE IT?' 'See

---

❏ The moral majority would have us believe that anal intercourse is the monopoly of gay men. According to the Kinsey Institute, 30-40% of females have engaged in anal intercourse. This, by the way, is the most frequently missed question (80%) on the Kinsey sex test.

WHAT?' I asked. 'His COCK,' they chimed, 'he's supposed to have a good 10 inches and he's very proud of it and loves to show it off."

Smokey Robinson. The legendary Motown soulster was spotted at the gym by one of my readers who reports that he is big and thick. And in her book about the Supremes, Mary Wilson writes about Smokey's huge "instrument."

Wayne Rogers. Handsome blond Princeton-graduate who co-starred in *M*A*S*H* and *Trapper John, MD*, there is no doubt as to his cocksmanship. In the television movie, *City of Angels*, there are several clear shots of his impressive endowment hanging down the left leg of a tight pair of brown slacks. The contour is unmistakable. Amazingly, the censors never caught this, but it certainly made my mouth water.

Billy Rose. Another showman of the early screen era who sported an enormous cock. Interestingly, both Billy and Milton Berle were married to the same woman, Joyce Matthews, who must have surely been dilated after taking on these horsehung studs for a number of years.

Porfirio Rubirosa. In *Poor Little Rich Girl*, C. David Heymann writes that "Rubirosa's prodigal dimensions were so widely and casually discussed that it became customary when ordering freshly ground pepper in the finest European restaurants to ask the waiter for the *Rubirosa*. The comparison of Rubirosa's natural equipment to a sixteen-inch carved pepper mill helps explain why he had women on several continents clamoring for his attention.

John Schneider. Big, blond, handsome crooner, and star of the forgettable *Dukes of Hazard*, John has a beautiful, pendulous 8" cock (20 cm).

Johnny "Oscar" Stamponato. The eponymous namesake of the Academy Award statuette, it is rumored that his erect penis is the same size as the oscar (13").

Parker Stevenson. Who can forget *Cheers* star Kirstie Alley's Emmy award acceptance speech--"I want to thank my husband for giving me the big one for the past 8 years." Big indeed it is, and in one of her special television interview programs, Barbara Walters asked what Kirstie meant when she said "the big one." Kirstie giggled, and simply replied, "It's **BIG!!!**"

Shadoe Stevens. One reader of *Fact and Phallusy* writes that Stevens, the host of the weekly radio countdown show "American Top 40," "was formerly

---

❏ It is rumored that after his murder, Rasputin's 13" penis was hacked off. It was allegedly kept in a velvet-lined box on top of a bureau of an admirer for many years.

spokesman for Federated Stores. He used the name of 'Fred Rated' and used to do all sorts of zany antics in their commercials. I watched one where he came out with a big hammer and broke a TV set. He was wearing white trousers and I couldn't believe what it was. He hung halfway to his knee. He's a good 8" (20 cm) flaccid."

Donald Sutherland. Fellini, when casting for *Casanova*, wanted a real cocksman, and cast Sutherland--who allegedly sports 9" (22 cm) for the role.

Franchot Tone. A talented comedian and actor in *Mutiny on the Bounty* and other swashbuckler movies, Tone was known to have his offscreen romances pay homage to his phallic monument before buggering them. He was married for a time to Joan Crawford, one of Hollywood's most notorious size queens, who described him as "a ten inch cocksman who compelled his women to pay homage to his shaft before buttfucking them. They don't make them like that anymore."

Forrest Tucker. The late actor and star of television's zany sitcom, *F Troop* sported one of the thickest, beefiest, and longest penises of all. "Tuck" along with his friends Milton Berle and comedian Harry Ritz founded *The Long Schlong Club of Bel Air*. The standing rule of the club was that one must be hung at least 10" (25 cm) to join. In the movie *Auntie Mame* with Rosilind Russell, there is a scene with Tuck walking beside his horse in a pair of crisply-ironed jodhpurs. The outline of his horsecock is clearly visible. Tuck was understandably proud of his phallic leviathan (which allegedly measured 8" soft and 10" hard) and his membership in the Lakeside Golf Club gave him opportunities to show off his prize-winning knockwurst. When he and his wife attended social functions, folks in the know would discreetly point and make phallic gestures with hands spread a foot apart. Writer James Bacon pens the following humorous anecdote:

> Members with guests, especially with out-of-town guests, never fail to visit the sleeping Tuck. Mr. Tucker would nap on the massage table in the locker room while envious men ventured a peek. Bacon adds, ''I was in the locker room dressing one day when a group of six people sauntered by the massage table. The club member, an airline executive, lifted the towel and commented: 'Now you will really have something to tell the folks back home. Fuck the Grand Canyon!'

❏   Legendary rock guitarist Jimi Hendrix allegedly had his large penis cast in plaster. Several specimens are said to adorn the mantels of devoted fans.

Robert Wagner. I received this letter from a reader in 1992:

> I was visiting Winchester, VA for their annual Apple Blossom Festival held in May of each year. This was several years ago when Robert Wagner was the Grand Marshal. I had a float in the parade and while waiting in line we were close to a small church on one of the streets waiting to enter the parade. I needed to get to a bathroom to void myself. I noticed this church on the corner. I got out of my car, went over to the church to see if it was open, and went in to use the men's room. As I was standing there at the urinal, in came Mr. Wagner and asked if I cared if he shared the urinal because things were about to move in the parade line. There the two of us stood at the same urinal with our penises in our hands. I glanced over and never in my years on this earth have I seen a larger penis hanging out of a fitted suit trousers. Flaccid yes, and I know it would have measured between 8-9'' (20-22 cm) and to me compared to my prize it looked more like a piece of sausage hanging out of his trousers. He finished, I finished...and I really was quite surprised when he looked up and said thanks for sharing your urinal.

Clint Walker. This tall, handsome actor with the sensuous basso profundo voice emanates virility from every pore. In the 1950s he used to work out at "Vince's Gym" in the San Fernando Valley. A friend of his reports that Clint brandishes a thick, uncut, veiny cock that matches his barrel-chested build.

James "Skip" Ward. Onetime golden boy of Hollywood and co-star of the cult classic *Night of the Iguana* (1964) measures in at a thick 8" (20 cm).

James Woods. The talented actor with the cantankerous, irascible reputation on the set is known as one of the King Cocks of Hollywood. Recently, Woods became involved in a romantic tiff with his girlfriend, who kneed him in the crotch. Woods decided to file assault charges, but needed evidence, so he enlisted the services of a production assistant to take a photograph of his injured genitals. Copies of this secret Polaroid are now making the rounds, and the word is out about his foot-long firehose. Ex-girlfriend Shawn Young once commented that Woods would be a better person "if only God had given him a small penis."

Darryl F. Zanuck. Legendary movie producer, Zanuck's short compact body belied his monstrous kielbasa. He had scores of affairs with leading ladies and made Linda Darnell a star largely because she turned out to be such a

---

❏ How does man's 6" (15 cm.) penis stand up to other members of the animal kingdom? The gorilla = 3" (8 cm.), the wild boar = 18" (45 cm.), the horse = 30" (75 cm.), the elephant = 80" (200 cm.), the blue whale = 96" (240 cm.).

talented fellatrix. He cast a lot of women based on how well they screwed and one of his practices was to audition budding starlets by unzipping his fly, plopping his foot-long meatloaf on his desk and commanding them to "suck it." If they weren't shocked out of their skulls, they frequently were rewarded with a part. Zanuck made no bones about his cocksmanship, proclaiming "baby, I'm the biggest and the best!" In his biography of Zanuck, Leonard Mosley writes: "Everybody talked about it in Hollywood and the rumor was that his prowess as a cocksman was just unbelievable...Zanuck had a body like a bantam cock, very stringy, but also strong."

Artists

Henri De Toulouse-Lautrec. His growth stunted by a crippling childhood malady, the great French artist who befriended prostitutes barely achieved five feet in height. His genitals were abnormally large, even for a man of ordinary stature. Commenting on his fubsy body and oversized cock, he referred to himself as "a coffeepot with a big spout." His close friends used to refer to his outsized organ as a "verge à pattes" (walking penis).

Politicians

Lyndon Baines Johnson. Horsemen might be interested in knowing that LBJ may have had the crown champion of presidential cocks. The press corps in the Washington of his time can confirm this. Not remembered for his tact or decorum, LBJ was known to invite the press (all male at the time) into his bathroom (*TIME* magazine states that he conducted briefing sessions from his toilet!) or his private swimming pool. Johnson was fond of intimidating his subordinates and rivals--mentally, physically, and sexually. In the middle of a meeting, he was known to capriciously invite his Cabinet members for a swim. LBJ was the first to disrobe, but he wouldn't enter the pool until the last man had removed (reluctantly) his clothes. Speaking off the record, one former politician reported that during one of these spontaneous swim sessions, Johnson icily stared at his acolytes after everyone had stripped. Shaking his horse-sized cock at his subordinates, he threatened "if any of this gets out, you're finished."

❏ *The Hung Jury* is a strictly heterosexual dating club that matches well-endowed men (8" / 20 cm+) with their female admirers. For a sample issue of their newsletter, "Measuring Up," send $10 + self-addressed, business-size envelope to: P.O. Box 417, Los Angeles, CA 90078.

Charles Robb. The masculine, handsome, and intelligent former governor of Virginia is also the husband of LBJ's daughter. Robb is known to sport an unusually-thick 8-incher that requires two hands to encircle. His lucky sons are undoubtedly hung like horses, having inherited big-dick genes from grandfather LBJ as well.

John Warner. Influential senator from Virginia and former Secretary of the Navy, he was married to Liz Taylor who once asked the sales clerk of a posh Rodeo Drive boutique to help her locate some briefs with an extra large pouch for her heavily-hung husband.

Authors

Lord Byron. Immortal genius of English literature, Byron's reputation as a libertine (sexual liaisons with boys, women, and even his half-sister, according to writer Leigh W. Rutledge) kept him from being buried in Poet's Corner in Westminster Abbey. In 1938, 114 years after his death, the casket was exhumed and his body was found to be in a remarkably well-preserved state. One of the observers remarked that "his sexual organ shewed quite abnormal development."

Noel Coward. A reader claims to have been seduced by the award-winning playwright at a 1945 party in Bermuda. "He was hung like a Clydesdale Stallion," writes the seduced, "I remain dilated to his size."

Jack London. Muscular and handsome author of the classics *White Fang* and *Call of the Wild*, London was affectionately referred to as "The Stallion" by his friends.

Alexander Pushkin. The fact that this celebrated Russian poet was part black helped fuel the rumors of his endowment status through the literary circles of St. Petersburg.

Musicians

Eddie Arnold. One of the original Country/Western superstars, this Grand Ole Opry staple is said to brandish the biggest, longest, and fattest dick on the prairie--or anywhere else for that matter. Arnold delighted in comparing his, ahem, talent with other members of the band. Best guesses place his legendary endowment at 10 1/2".

David Cassidy. With monster phallic genes inherited from dad Jack Cassidy, it was inevitable that son David would be a "chip off the old block." Despite his diminuitive stature, the former teen idol and star of *The Partridge Family* makes no effort to downplay his equine organ. In his book, *Come on get happy*, he makes liberal mention of his monster cock. There is a semi-revealing photo taken of David wearing tight pants. The outline of his endowment is unmistakable. *Rolling Stone* magazine even ran nude photos of him shot by legendary shutterbug Annie Leibowitz. James Bacon's book, *Hollywood is a Four-Letter Town* also makes liberal reference to Cassidy's legendary size.

Shawn Cassidy. David isn't the only Cassidy boy with a lot to crow about. Younger brother Shawn, a teen hearththrob in the late 1970s and singer of the #1 hit *Da Do Ron Ron*, also brandishes a pubic python between his legs. A reader of an earlier edition of this book claims to have met Shawn in *Embers* Disco in Portland, Oregon several years ago. They became acquainted and retired to his Lake Oswego condo. "When he became aroused, I was extremely surprised. I've never seen a cock so thick, and I've seen hundreds of hard cocks. I could not encircle his cock with my hand, and I have large hands...a good approximation of his size is 8" (20 cm) in circumference and 9 - 9 1/2" (22-23 cm) in length."

Adam Clayton. According to a guest on *The Joan Rivers Show*, this member of the celebrated rock band *U2* is so well hung that an album cover had to be redesigned to cover up his obvious endowment.

Dick Haymes. Big band singer of the 1940s and one-time husband of Rita Hayworth, it is claimed that he sported a whopping 10-incher (25 cm).

Levon Helm. Founding member of *The Band*, Helm has appeared in several movies including *Coal Miner's Daughter* with Cissy Spacek. One rock magazine made blatant mention of his "outsized genitals."

❏ Among some Orthodox Jews, it is important to show that blood is drawn during the circumcision ritual. To make sure that the operation was performed correctly, the rabbi invites an honored guest to apply his lips to the baby's penis to suck off the blood. This is known as *Metzitzah.*

Jimi Hendrix. Rock's premier psychedelic guitarist was hung like a bull. Scores of groupies spread the word that his cock was "damn near as big as his guitar." In the 1960s, a gaggle of cock-hungry Chicago groupies, who called themselves *The Plaster Casters*, acquired an unusual hobby--of taking plaster casts of their rock idol's penises. Jimi Hendrix was only too happy to accommodate their request, and several replicas of his penis can still be found floating around, attesting to his immenseness. True to his reputation as a legendary cocksman, the Whisky A Go-Go once offered a Jimi Hendrix sandwich consisting of "a Polish sausage on a wa-wa bun."

Jim Kerr. Singer with the Australian rock band, *Simple Minds*, one former lover remarked "I have to confess, I'd never seen anything quite like it."

Tom Jones. Aging gracefully, he still manages to pack in arenas full of screaming middle-aged marms. Loyal fans fight for front row tickets to get a glimpse of that legendary bulge in his peter-pinching tights. On a recent Howard Stern TV show, Tom Jones was featured as a guest. Tom volunteered that he was uncut and very large. When at the gym, he added, many men admire his equipment. He also mentioned that once Milton Berle decided to show him what he had and Jones was very impressed.

Huey Lewis. Legendary groupie "Sweet Connie" (memorialized in Grand Funk's 1974 smash *We're an American Band*) has slept with dozens of rock stars. She comments that Huey Lewis has the King Cock in the world of Rock. Want to see for yourself? Rent a copy of Robert Altman's *Short Cuts*, in which you can watch Huey in an historic full-frontal urination scene.

Frank Sinatra. According to writer Jim Boyd, who interviewed Sinatra biographer Jane Ellen Wayne, "When Ava Gardner and Grace Kelly were on location in Africa shooting *Mogambo*, Gardner took the future Princess on a tour of the various native villages and was bold enough to lift up the breeches of the men, exposing their cocks. With each man she inspected with Kelly by her side, Ava would comment: 'Nope...not as big as Frank's'."

In James Spada's biography on Grace Kelly, Gore Vidal offers a similar account of the incident: "The location was full of these tall Watusis, beautiful warriors who had been hired as extras, wearing their breechclouts. The girls were walking along, and Ava said to Grace, 'I wonder if their cocks are as big as people say? Have you ever seen a black cock?' Grace turned purple, of course, and said 'Stop that, don't talk like that!' Ava said, 'That's

---

❑   Kinsey reports the case of a man who had three orgasms a day over a period of 30 years.

funny...neither have I'--and with that she reached over and pulled up the breechclout of one of the Watusis, who gave a big grin as this huge cock flopped out. By then Grace had turned absolutely blue. Ava let go of the breechclout, turned to Grace, and said, 'Frank's bigger than that.'"

Rex Smith. Singing star *(You take my breath away)* and lead in *Pirates of Penzance* (1983), Smith's cock is legend, and I'm told that he makes NO attempt to conceal those 9 1/2 (23 cm) inches backstage or on a date.

Randy Travis. Country heartthrob is said to sport an impressive 8 1/2-incher (21 cm).

Andy Williams. Popular 60s crooner ("Moon River") who now has his own performance theater in Branson, Missouri, makes our list for the first time. A former chauffeur of Mr. Williams commented, "Tom J. (another popular singer) stuffed his pants with a sock. Andy Williams didn't have to."

Athletes

Jim Brown. This former football great-turned-actor is one man who keeps the "blacks are hung bigger" myth alive. Through his alleged affairs with Raquel Welch (during filming of *100 Rifles*) and Jacqueline Bisset, rumors abounded of his astounding endowment, which are reportely in the 9" (22 cm) x 8" (20 cm) range.

Food for cock

A species of fetid mushroom *(phallales)* known as the "stinkwort," closely resembles the male member. In Japan, where it is considered a delicacy, it is often served in soup and supposedly increases a man's virility.

❑ The average male averages 4-5 nocturnal erections during sleep every night. Each erection generally occurs about 90 minutes apart.

The secret sex lives
of your favorite celebrities

Ever wonder if your favorite athlete, musician, movie star, or politician is circumcised or not? Perhaps you wonder how he measures up. Movie industry veteran Chuck Thompson has conducted a 15-year research project that details the circumcision status of more than 2,000 celebrities (and growing). This list was once featured on *Phil Donahue*, who noted a glaring error--his own! On national television, Phil read from the list of uncircumcised celebrities and found his name. "Here I am, right above Troy Donahue," he quipped, "And they're wrong!" Phil admitted on national TV that he had been circumcised as a child.

Chuck has been intimately involved in the motion picture business for years and knows many of the stars personally. In addition, he has a number of "scouts" and "researchers" in the industry who keep their eyes open for new reports to add to the list. Other details, such as cock size, are provided when eye-witness accounts are available.

Interest in this project has been so overwhelming that Chuck began publishing a quarterly newsletter providing intimate details of the sex lives of the world's most prominent celebrities. Once you see the dynamite (and sometimes shocking) contents of these newsletters, you'll want to order the back issues as well. Send $10 for the master list and/or $5 for a sample newsletter ($15 for both) to:

Chuck Thompson

P.O. Box 691024

Hollywood, CA 90069

Joe Pepitone. Former member of the New York Yankees, baseball great Pepitone does indeed brandish an impressive sausage. The photo in my private collection shows Joe to be the proud owner of a size 8.

Wilt Chamberlain. *The Stilt* more accurately describes the foot-long pole between his legs. At the height of his popularity in the early 1970s, the basketball legend attended a number of parties in which he proudly displayed his amazing phallus to interested females.

Historical Figures

Prince Albert. Husband of Queen Victoria, rumors of his mammoth cock are legion. Many of his intimate associates claim that it was indeed stallion size.

John Dillinger. Folk hero and famed gangster of the 1930s, Dillinger relished the rumors that circulated of his 18" (45 cm) penis. There are two versions to the story. A physician who attended to the autopsy, proclaimed that he was of average endowment. However, three different individuals have written to me, claiming that they have seen Dillinger's foot-long penis in a hidden back room of the Smithsonian Institute, carefully preserved in formaldehyde in a glass container. The Smithsonian still receives about a hundred inquiries a year to see the legendary phallus. No one is able to explain why his penis was amputated prior to his burial.

Grigori Rasputin. The enigmatic "Mad Monk of Russia" who ingratiated himself with the Royal family was a charismatic man who mesmerized all those around him. Women and men alike swooned at the sight of him. His sexual prowess was as overpowering as his charm and charisma. Legend has it that he entertained as many as 20 women a night. A peculiar knobby wart adorned the base of his 12 3/4" (32 cm) penis. Strategically located at the pubic juncture, it acted as a clitoral tickler which titillated his partners, causing many to pass out from the orgasmic frenzy. He was assassinated in 1916 by Russian aristocrats, who poisoned, shot, buggered, castrated, and then drowned him. His gargantuan organ was then hacked off by his envious assailants. According to his biographer/daughter, an obsequiously-devoted follower absconded with the legendary schlong and adoringly preserved it in a velvet-lined keepsake box on top of her dresser for years.

❑ Hollywood Hunk Nick Nolte allegedly had a "testicle tuck." "My scrotum was sinking with age." he explained. "I went to see the doctor because I was fed up with sitting on my nuts."

Charles Stuart II. King of Great Britain (1660-1685) whose acolytes called him "Old Rowley," which also happened to be the name of his favorite studhorse. It was joked that his penis and scepter were of equal length. The poet Rochester was temporarily banished from court in 1676 for lampooning the royal penis.

Marshal Tito. The iron-fisted ruler of Yugoslavia from 1946 until his death in 1980, Josip Broz had enemies on all flanks. One disgruntled military figure spread rumors about Tito, claiming that he wore women's underwear and had been castrated. Nothing could be further from the truth. Tito, who was notoriously well-endowed, wore a bathing suit at a junta of major military leaders and inquired "Will you please ask Capt. Waugh why he thinks I am a lesbian?"

Contemporary figures of note

Mikhael Baryshnikov. "A thick 9 1/2" of Russian salami" claims a former paramour. If you look carefully at the magazine ads promoting his signature bodywear, a "candid" photo of thie dancer and his model strolling along a Long Island beachfront, you can see where retouch artists creatively rubbed out what a dance belt could have accomplished in a pre-shot.

Tom Brokaw. Boyishly-handsome TV news anchor with the deep, sexy voice. Older Angelenos still recall a younger Brokaw covering the devastating Sylmar earthquake of 1971 in form-fitting slacks along the, er, fault line. It seems the network woke Tom up pre-dawn, and well...he was up and ready for action before he knew it. I estimate his broadcast abilities to be a 9+. Another reader writes in to say "Last summer I personally observed Tom Brokaw urinating in the men's room at the Omaha, Nebraska airport and he proudly displayed a partially-erect, thick penis measuring by my estimation a very impressive 8" (20 cm).

Dick Cavett. Here's what Janis Joplin had to say about the glib talkshow host: "You'd never guess it, but Cavett has a much bigger cock and is a better lay than (Joe) Namath."

❑ Who had the smallest cock in Hollywood? Rumor has it that the King of the Westerns, an academy award winner (now deceased) whose initials are "J.W." sported a penis that measured barely 3" when erect.

Alexander Godunov. According to one anonymous individual: "The six-foot-four Russian ballet star-turned-actor when he's sober and can get it up, measures in at a thick 10 1/2" (26 cm).

Nicky Hilton. First husband of Elizabeth Taylor and (now deceased) heir to the Hilton fortune, it is said he's the man who "stretched" Liz so no other man could satisfy her, save Sen. John Warner--whose cock status is legendary. According to one anonymous Beverly Hills socialite, "Hilton is the only man Joan Collins couldn't er, uh, accommodate, and turned down when she saw his thick 11" erection."

Rudolf Nuryev. Life study photos of ballet star Nuryev taken by Richard Avedon for use as a guide in sculpture making shows him with a thick, pendulous uncut penis measuring a good 7" soft. Erect measurements top the rulers at between 8 and 9" (20-22 cm.).

Aristotle Onassis. Another man who was obsessively proud of his endowment, Ari often referred to his cyclopean shishkabob as "the secret of my success." He was so defensive about his reputation as a cocksman that he once pulled a reporter into a men's room to prove how well-endowed he was. And you always thought it was his billions that put the smile on Jackie O.'s face.

Dan Rather. One of the most respected men in journalism is also a true gentleman, often getting coffee for his subordinates. He is as hung as he is handsome and intelligent. A former paramour comments on his size and immense amount of body hair: "Going to bed with Dan was like going to bed with a shag rug. And he was HUGE!"

Steve Reeves. In a back issue of now defunct gay rag *QQ*, an article mentioned that this former Mr. Universe who starred in most of the early Hercules movies, sported an enormous cock that "swung back and forth like the trunk of an elephant" when he walked.

Chuck Yeager. The censors of his early Delco battery commercials apparently missed the fact that the first man to break the sound barrier showed an incredible salami hanging down the left leg of his flight suit. This is truly a man with "the right stuff."

❑ The smallest-endowed rock star? Groupie "Sweet Connie" tells us that the dishonor goes to "P.F.," (*Baby I love your way*) who had the biggest selling live album of the 1970s.

7

Penis Enlargement Methods

Now for the chapter you've been waiting for. I'm sure you're greeting this penis enlargement subject with a healthy degree of cynicism, as indeed you should. After all, psychologists and physicians have inculcated us for years with the notion that penis enlargement is impossible. But is it really?

Over the years, anthropologists have discovered ancient and not-so-ancient cultures that have practiced penis enlargement, yet this is seldom mentioned in modern scientific literature. As recently as 50 years ago, medical manuals openly discussed the possibility of penis enlargement. However, the puritanical moral climate severely restricted any serious investigation into such subjects. Fortunately, the sexual revolution has forced us to re-evaluate the way we view the human body, and grassroots progress is being made in the study and understanding of the male organ. Although the medical establishment continues to claim that penis enlargement is impossible, there are hundreds of men, who through personal experience can easily refute this claim, and we will read many of their case histories (including those of three physicians) in the coming pages.

❏ The left testicle hangs lower in right handed man. The opposite seems to be true for left-handed men. This keeps the two balls from squeezing against each other when the man sits down.

Penis enlargement methods run the gamut, from the logical to the ridiculous. Nevertheless, I will present the most popular methods which have been practiced through the ages, including several fascinating (and promising) methods that have come to my attention recently. These methods are provided for information purposes only. Any medical advice must be secured from a licensed physician. If you choose to try any of these methods, you do so by your own volition. Nevertheless, I am interested in your success (or lack of it). Write to me of your experiences with any of the following methods. If you know of others that have not been reported here, please write with the complete details so that it can be evaluated by our research team and reported on for the next issue of this book.

For the convenience of categorization, the penis enlargement methods have been divided into the following rubrics:

❑   Manual Methods

❑   Mental/Visual Imagery Methods

❑   Genetic Manipulation

❑   Surgical Methods

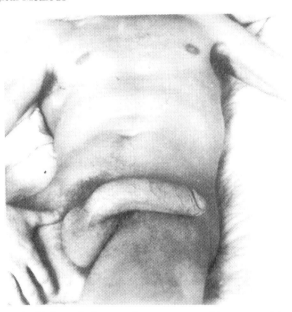

A thick penis has much greater stretching potential

❑   The average ejaculation consists of about a teaspoon of semen.

92

MANUAL METHODS

The following methods involve manual manipulation of the penis in one form or another. Most of the ritualistic methods of penis elongation found in different cultures and tribal societies of the world involve repeated manipulation of the genitals with the hands or auxiliary devices.

Polynesian stretch method

Pioneer cultural anthropologist Margaret Mead, author of *Coming of Age in Samoa* reported that Polynesian males stretch their penises with a woven device of plant fibers similar to a "Chinese finger trap." The penis is inserted into one end of this tube while a weighted object is hung from the other end.

Conclusion: Mead doesn't go into great depth into the methodology, nevertheless this method of hanging a device from the penis to increase its length is the oldest enlargement trick known to man and is found among dozens of primitive cultures around the world. Physiologically, the effect of hanging a heavy weight from the penis encourages a relaxation of the suspensory ligament, which can ultimately externalize an additional inch or so of the *crura*-or penile root. The Polynesians apparently engage in this activity on a casual basis, for little genuine enlargement is noted, as evidenced by their modest erect penile dimensions which average 5" (12.5 cm).

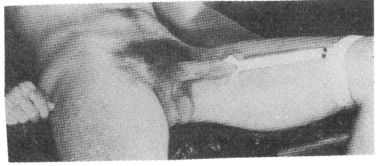

A "Super Stretcher" device--a product of dubious penis enlargement value.

❏ Over his lifetime, the average male will produce about 18 quarts (17 liters) of semen.

93

P.L.D.™

The newest entrant to this book is a variation of one of the oldest penis enlargement techniques around. Taking a clue from the Indian Sadhus, Peruvian Cholomecs, and Cook Islanders--all of whom append weights from their penises--entrepreneur Roland Clark developed a high-tech device that could be comfortably worn from the penis while increasing the length.

Mr. Clark is well known in the foreskin restoration underground, where his P.U.D.™ (Penile Uncircumcising Device) has become the best-selling product for non-surgically restoring the foreskin. Many of his clients wrote, mentioning that their penises had lengthened 1/2" or more after wearing the weighted P.U.D.™ device for six months or more. This was an unexpected side-effect. With this in mind, Roland developed a totally new device that was specifically intended for lengthening the penis.

Modular in design, the P.L.D.™ consists of two 4 oz. end pieces and two 12 oz. center pieces. All can be worn together or separately. The amount of weight worn largely depends upon the size of the wearer's penis. Larger penises naturally can tolerate greater weight. What truly sets this device apart from other "pretenders" is the method of application. A loop of soft surgical tubing is slipped through the holes in the weights to create a "noose." This noose is then slipped over the head of the penis and tightened slightly behind the coronal ridge. As the weight can feasibly damage the sensitive nerve bundle in the penis if worn for a long period of time, the manufacturer recommends that the P.L.D.™ be worn only for two hours a day--20 minutes on and 20 minutes off. One should be standing when wearing the device so that gravity can do its work on the suspensory ligament. As little as 4 oz. can be worn or as much as 32 oz. It can be worn under clothing, but most men choose to wear it in the privacy of their own homes. Naturally a pendulous series of weights dangling from the penis is not easy to hide under a pair of pants, so public wearing may not be advisable.

This device has become a popular adjunct to penis lengthening surgery. Many urologists now fit their patients with the P.L.D.™ device after surgery to help the penis to heal at its maximum new length. Roland Clark mentioned that after wearing the device a few months, his girlfriend begged him to stop wearing the device--his penis was getting too long!

❏   Approximately 1 in 100,000 males is born with a diphallus--or double penis!

Conclusion: This is an ago-old technique with a new facelift. Stretching the suspensory ligament is a proven method of lengthening the penis. One must be judicious when wearing the P.L.D.™ so as to not damage the sensitive nerve bundle in the penis. When worn 15-20 minutes per session (for approximately 2 hours per day) the penis can safely and permanently lengthen over a period of months--the precise amount of time depends upon your individual anatomy. The P.L.D.™ kit sells for approximately $150 and includes a draw-string carrying bag, four modular weights, a length of surgical tubing, an applicator bar, and instructions. An instructional video (optional purchase) is also available. To request a brochure or to order, call American Bodycrafters at (800) 628-1852 or (714) 374-0646 or write to P.O. Box 7555, Huntington Beach, CA 92615.

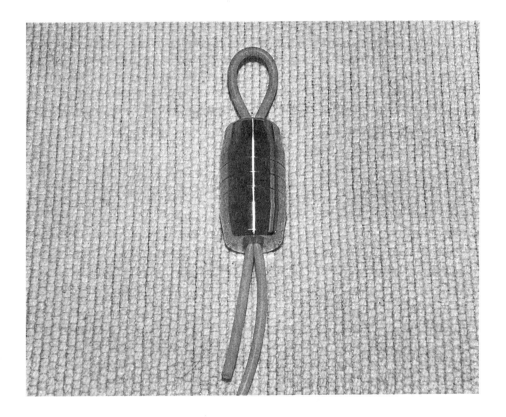

❏ Beverly Hills urologist James Elist, MD has developed a new technique for permanently enlarging the testicles. A prosthesis, which comes in three sizes, is surgically implanted next to the testes. Cost? $2,500.

The Penicure Method

Walter Schlesinger, M.D., is one of a growing number of physicians who refute the claim that the penis cannot be enlarged. In his book, *Penicure, the Manhood Miracle,* Dr. Schlesinger writes:

> It is possible to increase the size of your penis through exercise. The exercise consists primarily of grasping the penis gently and stretching it half a dozen times or so several times a day. Such an exercise could be performed when it is necessary to urinate. This will serve as a reminder and obviate any need for special occasions. Instead of stretching the penis a given number of times, the husband may continue the exercise until the organ starts to stiffen due to the manipulaton. This is best accomplished by grasping the head with three fingers and gently stretching the shaft. Over a period of several months, this exercise may add a half inch or more to the length of the penis.

Stephen T. Chang, M.D. concurs that the deliberate stretching of one's penis encourages it to grow. In *The Tao of Sexology,* he writes:

> The size and shape of the penis, although determined at birth, can be improved upon. The male body may stop growing at the age of 30, but the penis continues to grow. Through scientific study, we know that the penis grows until a man dies. The older a man is, the bigger his penis becomes. It continues to grow in length and diameter, encouraged by the shaking and squeezing done after urination.

Yes, the penis, as well as the nose, ears, and other appendages, continues to grow throughout a man's lifetime, thanks mainly to the effects of gravity. However, this natural growth is miniscule, being measured in millimeters rather than inches. This simply means that a 6" penis at age 21 may grown to 6 1/4" by age 70. However, through repeated manipulation and stretching (as in the "Penicure" method and others that will be discussed shortly) natural penile growth may be encouraged even further. Conversely, lack of use may also cause the penis to atrophy slightly.

Conclusion: Repeated and deliberate pulling of the penis will help relax the suspensory ligament over time. The "Penicure" method has much in common with the Tao and Jelq methods (to be discussed shortly). Each involves daily exercises which force blood into the erectile bodies of the

---

❏   Sperm cells comprise less than 5% of the volume of semen.

penis (corpora cavernosa). The underlying principle suggests that through repeated and sustained engorgement, the penis can be increased in size. Through this simple exercise, which Dr. Schlesinger asserts need only be performed after urination, a half inch or more may be gained over time.

Indian Sadhu method

Along the upper reaches of the Ganges resides one of the most bizarre cults on Earth. Its adherents practice various forms of negation and asceticism, including body modification--much of which is too grotesque to mention here. Their Holy Men (Sadhus), believe that the spirit of God resides in the penis. They therefore practice various rituals to modify the penis in order to establish a spiritual connection with the phallic deities.

San Francisco advertising executive and self-confessed "modern primitive" Fakir Musafar (aka Roland Loomis) has practiced body modification for years. He is intimately familiar with the practices of primitive cultures that incorporate genital modification into their societal ethos, including the Sadhus. In the controversial book, *Modern Primitives,* he describes how the Sadhus elongate their penises to incredible lengths:

> They selected very young males...had progressively heavier weights hung on their cocks until they became stretched out incredibly long. When they reached adulthood, they carried it coiled up in a little basket and if they removed the basket, it would hang down below their knees. But they couldn't do this to too many males, because after the "treatment," they weren't able to impregnate, and then of course, the race would die out.

The underground film, *Dances Sacred and Profane* explicitly shows how this esoteric clan practices its surreptitious ritual:

> In our film we show some Indian Sadhus who have practiced the same weight training; they hang a little weight on their penis when they are pre-pubescent and leave it on all the time. As the formative ligament (which restricts the length of the penis) hasn't hardened, this stretches it. This practice has to be begun early in life or it won't work. After they get it to 8-9'', they can really...stretch it out to incredible lengths. The mature Sadhus' penises are tied in knots, but

❏   The function of pubic hair is to trap odors secreted by the apocrine glands. These odors serve as pheromones--or olfactory stimulators for the opposite sex.

97

usually there's a cloth wrapped around it. That was considered proper etiquette--they don't let it hang out there naked.

Fakir Musafar also mentions a plant extract they use to induce perpetual erections (which can be very dangerous) and to increase the girth of the penis:

> There's also a Tantric technique used in India called suka training (suka means swelling). This is a way of getting a hard-on that won't come down--you can keep it hard for hours, days, weeks, months! However, if you have an erection for too long, it becomes very hard to get it down, and it's also very painful. (Readers note: any erection that lasts longer than a few hours--known medically as priapism--can be extremely dangerous and ultimately result in gangrene). Through suka training men have made incredibly big cocks in India; they're manufactured--they're made. The people there have developed very interesting ways to modify the body that are very practical and that work. Like I said, our film, "Dances Sacred and Profane" had footage of Sadhus whose penises are wrappped up, but obviously they're about eighteen inches long.

> (To develop these penises) "they start early. A young man may start out with a triangular-shaped block of wood with a small hole, which he puts around his penis. He hangs little weights on it, adding just a few grams additionally every day, and wears it all day, every day. They let that hang on there continuously day and night for a long period of time--usually they dig a hole in the ground and sit there and it hangs down. Or, they may hang a loop of rope over the head of the organ and hang weights on that.

National Geographic has allegedly studied these people, and rumor has it that they possess a prodigious collection of photographs documenting these incredible cocks, but of course, modesty and general public priggishness toward anything phallic dictates that they never be published. Even in their native India, the Sadhus are considered aberrant mavericks and the government would just as soon that outsiders not know about them. A classic case of penis envy, no doubt.

Weight suspension seems to be the preferred enlargement method on the continent of Africa. Recently, a reader in San Francisco informed me that while stationed in Southern Egypt during World War II, he came across several Sudanese males who suspended rocks from their pendulous penises

---

❑ Man has the largest and thickest penis of all male primates.

as part of a culturally-accepted enlargement ritual. Further up the Nile, the Caramoja tribe of northern Uganda "elongate their penises by tying a weight on the end," according to Alexandra Parsons in **"Facts & Phalluses."**

"Sometimes they get so long that the men have to literally tie a knot in them."

Conclusion: From the extinct Cholomecs of Peru to the Sadhus of India, penis elongation through the suspension of increasingly heavy weights is practiced. Both cultures begin with very young males--around the age of 6. Progressively heavy stones are appended from the penis. Some individuals wear them for 12 or more hours per day and remove them to accommodate nocturnal erections, while others (especially the Sadhus) wear them continuously. In the latter case, the erectile bodies become so distended, that in time, they become completely nonfunctional. Some men have allegedly lengthened their penises from 18 - 36"

This rare photo show a Sadhu youth (left) undergoing penis training. Notice the oval-shaped weight hanging from the penis. By the time he reaches adulthood, his penis will approach 18" in length.

❏   An orgasm lasts 3-10 seconds, and the contractions occur about 0.8 seconds apart.

through a lifetime of weight suspension. This is clearly undesirable from any physical or functional standpoint. The useless organ becomes a thin, limp serpent, incapable of erection. The outlandish length dictates that the penis be tied in a knot and worn in a cloth basket around the waist.

A recent issue of a popular adult magazine advertised a "ball and chain" penis enlarger. They claim that by wearing the device, the penis can be lengthened over time. This may be true, but remember that such "penis training" takes many, many months for any permanent change. Also, given the anatomy of the male organ, it is difficult to hang anything from it without causing bruising or severe discomfort. Also, the realities of modern life make it extremely inconvenient to wear such a device during the workday. Obscuring such a device under a pair of trousers would be extremely difficult. In a nutshell, hanging weights from the penis does work, but requires a great deal of time, is uncomfortable, does not increase the girth, and may damage the erectile bodies. Such primitive methods are best left to tribal societies.

Tao Method

Based on Tao metaphysics, this Oriental philosophy involves a combination of spiritual concentration and genital manipulation. According to Tao sexuality, it is necessary to achieve a "hand-in-glove" fit to achieve true harmony in sexual relations. When a penis is paired with a vagina that is too loose and too long, the penis does not fit snugly, which results in insufficient friction for both partners. In such a situation, a penis enlargement therapy is indicated.

This method involves breathing exercises coupled with the methodical grasping and pulling of the penis with the right hand while applying pressure to the perineum with the three fingers of the left hand. Other exercises include rotating the erect penis, both clock- and counterclockwise, slapping the thigh with the erection, and dipping it in warm water. It is claimed that within a month or two, the dedicated individual may notice an increase of an inch or so in length.

Stephen T. Chang, M.D., asserts that the shape of the penis can be changed. He claims that the correct penis shape will have a profound effect upon the satisfaction received by the partner:

❑   The heart beats up to 140 beats per minute at orgasm.

The best penile shape is considered to be the ''mushroom'' shape. The so-called ''mushroom'' penis has structures that are best suited for satisfying a woman, namely a large head and a narrow shaft. The large head contributes to the desirability, because it provides the greatest amount of stimulation and it massages the sides of the vagina and G point thoroughly and efficiently.

The least desirable penis shape is considered to be the triangular or pencil shape, with a small pointed head and a wide shaft. It is much harder to satisfy a woman with a pencil-shaped penis. But you need not despair if you have this type of penis, because it is possible to change the shape.''

There are three exercises that will affect this gradual change, according to Dr. Chang:

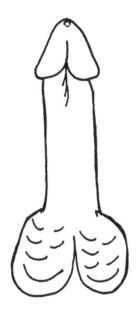

"Pencil-shaped penis"   "Mushroom-shaped penis"

❏   In New Delhi, India on February 3, 1991, The Association of Sex Educators, Counselors, and Therapists sponsored a three day "International Conference on Orgasm."

1) "Milk" the penis by squeezing and forcing the blood toward the glans. The head should become engorged with blood during this exercise. Over a period of time, the head should become larger and more prominent, gradually taking on the more desirable "mushroom shape."

2) Squeeze the shaft until it becomes rock-hard. Then release. This repeated squeezing and releasing will result in increasingly firmer erections.

3) After performing the first two exercises for several minutes, sit in a chair with feet on the floor and knees spread apart. Grasp the base of the penis and alternately slap the glans against each thigh. This should be done firmly, but not enough to cause discomfort or pain. This exercise will gradually strengthen the glans and increase its size and improve the shape while slightly desensitizing the organ. This gentle numbing of the nerve endings in the glans will enable the man to make love for longer periods of time by delaying ejaculation and resulting in vulcanic and powerful orgasms.

Mantak Chia is one of the preeminent practitioners of Taoist philosophy. In his book *Taoist Secrets of Love*, Chia provides precise instructions as how to enlarge and elongate your penis:

> Inhale the air through the nose into the throat...from there swallow and press it down to the stomach. Do not keep it in the chest. Then the air, which you may experience as energy, is imagined as a ball, and is rolled down the front of the body beneath the abdominal muscles. When the air reaches the lower-most part of the abdomen, press it into the penis itself. As you direct the air to the penis take 3 middle fingers of the left hand and press them to the Hui-Yin midpoint between the anus and the scrotum. This pressure prevents the air power from flowing back into the body. The power lodges in the penis itself.

> Resume normal breathing while keeping the left fingers on the Hui Yin midpoint. At the same time begin to directly exercise the penis. Pull it forward and backward, stretching it out in a smooth rhythmical movement for 36 times. Next use your thumb to rub the glans of the penis. This should erect the penis. If there is no erection, continue to pull and rub the glans until the penis stands.

> The right hand then circles the penis firmly at its base and, while holding firmly, slides forward about an inch. In this way the air energy is locked into the body of the penis itself and driven toward

❏   In Ancient Greece phallic fertility processions known as *phallophoriai* were held in which giant carved phalluses were carried by "penis bearers."

the tip of the head. Feel the pressure pushing forward toward the head and maintain it but don't force it too hard. Then the penis is pulled out to the right and rotated with a stirring action 36 times clockwise and counterclockwise. Then it is pulled out to the left and rotated another 36 times clockwise and counterclock- wise. Simultaneously maintain the outward pressure locks in the air.

This exercise massages the entire urogential system including the penis, the prostate gland, and the veins, arteries, and surrounding nerves; the bladder and even the kidney are beneficially stimulated. The energy of many bodily organs flows into the penis, and the tone and function of all are enhanced. In the final penile manipulation, gently beat the inner right thigh with the erect penis 36 times, while simultaneously maintaining the air-lock pull. Then beat the inner left thigh 36 times.

Finally, Chia advises the enlarger to soak the penis in warm water for one minute. He claims that this will help the organ absorb the warmth of the yang energy, thereby encouraging it to expand. He asserts that by following these exercises, a man can expect to experience a growth of an inch during the first month or so of practice. Further gains may be noticed, he adds, depending upon the individual's bodily structure. I contacted a master herbalist and student of Tao philosophy about this technique. He commented:

> This method (of penis enlargement) is from the pen of Master Mantak Chia, the most distinguished practitioner in the U.S., Canada, & Europe. Anything which he writes I take with the greatest seriousness. I would probably use this technique together with the enlargement herbs.

When I expressed doubt about the ability of this method to truly increase the size of the organ, he commented:

> I do not feel that your criticism of the technique is necessarily valid. One must keep in mind that this is more a Taoist than a Chinese technique. The Taoists were an elite band of men who practiced the most esoteric arts and sciences. Their knowledge was not shared with the common people. The Taoists, by the nature of their elevated knowledge, had favorable connections with the imperial household, the aristocracy and the ruling classes.

❏ The words "gymnastics" and "gymnasium" come from the Greek word *gymnos*, meaning "naked." Participation in athletic competition was usually performed in the nude.

Conclusion: This enigmatic method is fascinating on one hand but of dubious value on the other. Indeed, the Orient is redolent with salubrious secrets long repudiated by the West (acupuncture, herbal medicine, meditation), and we are slowly coming around, discovering that many of these "secrets" have great validity after all. As far as enlarging the penis, I have received letters from two different men who claim to have gained 1-3" through this method. However, before and after photos were not provided for proof. Also, considering that there are millions of Asian practitioners of Taoist philosophy, I find it amusing that there is a dearth of endowed Oriental males. If this method is so effective, then where are the masses of Taoist devotees with equine penises? My research team is still interested in taking the first case study of a Tao enlargee (with before and after photographs).

The Milking Method

The August 1989 issue of *Players* magazine contained an article by Donna Powell ("Making it Bigger") which provided instructions on how to increase the size of the penis. This is a very simple method involving a milking procedure that is specifically designed to "enlarge the size of your fibrous tissues and (penile) sinuses." Amazingly, the writer (a woman) claims that the male "WILL gain from half an inch to an inch within four to six weeks if you persistently perform the method...Some males have, within a year, nearly doubled the length of both their flaccid and erect penises."

In order to achieve optimal results, the penis must be neither flaccid nor erect. "Neither a soft shaft or a hard shaft are in the proper state to respond to any kind of development method," writes Ms. Powell. "The state which most males refer to as a "semi hard-on" is necessary before penis milking can cause 'tissue hypertrophy' and consequent enlargement. 'Penis milking' is simply a form of 'exercise' which inevitably works to enlarge the fibrous tissues and sinuses in the penis," she adds.

Here is their prescription for correctly performing the "milking procedure:"

> The male should be nude (at least from the waist down) and it is
> preferable that he stand in front of a mirror. A liberal dab of vaseline
> or hand cream MUST be applied to the flaccid penis at the beginning

---

❑ In 1990, the circumcision rate in the U.S. fell to 56% from a high of 90% in the 1960s.

in order to lubricate it for the vigorous milking. Using the thumb and forefinger (somewhat firmly, but not too firmly at first) downwards to the head. Within a short time the flaccid penis will develop partial tumescence, then your milkings should be performed with both hands, first one and then the other in a sort of rhythmic motion. After partial tumescence is achieved you should complete only fifty vigorous, firm-gripped milkings for the first five days; then after two days rest, increase your firm milkings to one hundred movements. You will notice, even after the first session, that your penis appears longer. It is, to some slight degree! But that 'slight degree' will add up measurably within less than a month and you will be well on the way to possessing a much larger member.

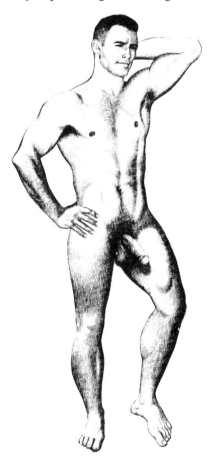

They advise the enlarger to shake the penis up and down from 25-50 repetitions after the milking exercises to limber up and relax the connective tissues. Once the individual has achieved the desired size (from several months to a year, they claim) the milking may be performed on a less frequent basis--perhaps once a week. They add that the man's age and size makes no difference. The key is to engage in the exercises with only a PARTIAL erection. The ideal time to do this is before a shower. If Vaseline is used, this can also be performed DURING the shower--the warm water helping to increase circulation to the penis. This method is further detailed in Alan Hull Walton's book **"Aphrodisiacs: From Legend to Prescription."**

❏ In Ancient Greece, women were used solely for procreation. Men sought sexual gratification from concubines and young men. To provide redress to the women's unmet needs, legislator Solon in 600 B.C., decreed that a husband was obligated to have sex with his wife at least 3 times a month.

Conclusion: This is one method that certainly has merit. Penis milking is one of the "secrets" of the Sudanese Arabs and is a major component of the Chartham method. My only beef is with the rapid gains alleged by Ms. Powell. Several dozen of my readers have engaged in a daily regimen of milking, but do not report permanent gains until after six months or so. I seriously dispute the claim of a 1/2" - 1" increase in only one month. It just will not happen. Also, it is extremely unlikely that more than an inch will ever be gained and the doubling of length in a year is sheer hyperbole. A size 5 will NOT magically grow to a size 10 in a year. It is interesting to note that no before and after photos accompanied the article. And why is a woman writing about this method? Does she have first hand experience? No, you won't get an inch increase in four weeks, but with a regular regimen (5 days a week), results will be noticed in most men in around 6 months. The problem is that most men get discouraged after 6-8 weeks and stop the exercises. Remember that progress in penis enlargement is agonizingly slow. If you are intent upon enlargement, you must be dedicated and be prepared to devote 15-20 minutes per day (at least five times a week) to this method.

Tibetan Monk method

I learned about this obscure practice from a reader who served in the Marine Corps in Vietnam. He was captured by the Viet Cong and held as a P.O.W. for several years. During his captivity, he observed the enormous penises of several visiting Tibetan monks and writes what he learned about their fascinatingly cryptic ritual:

> When I was in Vietnam and was a POW, some Tibetan monks came for a visit, and I swear, they had the largest dicks I had ever seen, and I haven't seen any to beat them yet. They were kind of like the guy you sent a photo of (readers--see photo on next page). They say they start when they are about 11, beginning the enlargement process, and one of them who could speak pretty good English told me some about how it was done. It was a sort of pulling and stretching process, done regularly, and then they start the young ones off fucking the older ones, and sucking each other quite often--I mean 4 or 5 times a day.

❏   In 14th century Europe, it was accepted practice for the newlywed couple to be accompanied to bed by a priest and family members who blessed the couple prior to their sexual union. The next morning, the bloody bedsheets were displayed as proof of their successful sexual encounter.

Most of the Vietnamese guys had very small dicks, and they were fascinated by how much larger most of us were than them, and they were all uncut so those of us who had big heads with no skin over them were something they liked. Of course, we hated the Viet Cong so much, it wasn't fun to be forced to have sex with them. You don't hear much about this from Vietnam vets because I imagine, they don't want anybody to think they had sex with another man, even if by force.

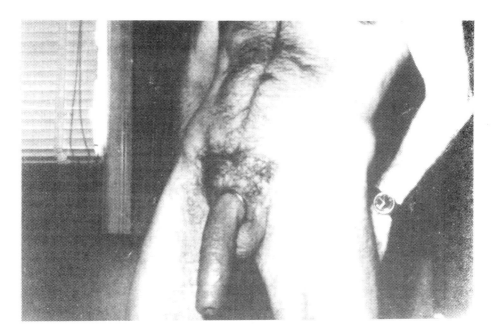

A true "donkey dick" that measures 10" x 7" (25 cm x 18 cm) when erect.

Conclusion: The details are sketchy, but it appears that the Tibetan Monks used a variation of the "milking" method described above. The homosexual acts are purely incidental and probably only serve to keep the penis in a state of near-continual tumescence. This story is nothing short of shocking, and it indeed would be the ultimate act of humiliation and degradation to be forced to have sex with the enemy--especially for a heterosexual man. Undoubtedly, this is the reason we haven't heard more about this. In fact, most Vietnam vets have probably blanked out all such memories.

❑ In Victorian society, all forms of sex--except for procreation--were considered vile. A myriad of devices were developed to keep young children from masturbating. In 1908, a nurse patented a cage-like device worn over the genitals with protruding spikes and locked in place with a key.

This story comes from a very credible source--a happily-married Southern gentleman with seven sons. It has taken more than two decades to put the horrific memories of Vietnam behind him, and only recently is he finally able to discuss some of his experiences there. It is unknown what Tibetan monks were doing in Vietnam, and I find it surprising to hear of Asian men with such large phalli. In my years of living in the Orient, I had never met an Asian male with an erect penis longer than 7". Perhaps this is a pleasant exception.

Hyperemiation/Vacuum Pumping

Vacuum pumping is experiencing a phenomenal surge of popularity as an adjunct to safe sex on both sides of the Atlantic. The fundamental principle is very simple. By creating a negative pressure around the penis (via the use of a vacuum), blood is forced into the organ which then becomes distended and turgid. Medically, this process is known as "hyperemiation."

When you get an erection, blood rushes into the two major tissues of the penis--the *corpora cavernosa* and the *corpus spongeosum*. These two sets of tissues fill up with blood much as a bicycle tire inflates with air and becomes rigid.

When using a vacuum pump, the blood in the penis becomes trapped, thereby fully engorging the tissues. The fundamental principle of enlargement through hyperemiation is predicated upon the ability to maintain the penis in an engorged state for relatively long period ot time--usually 30 minutes to an hour. Through repetitive hyperemiation, the phallic muscles and tissues are actually given a "workout." *Inches* magazine ran a feature article on vacuum pumping in their April 1989 edition. This is their version of how the process works:

> The muscle is actually 'torn down' in the process and rebuilds during the next day or so. Reworking the muscle in the same manner via the vacuum pump, repeatedly, is the same principle used in bodybuilding, stressing out the individual muscles and letting them rebuild into stronger, larger muscles.

> The major difference between what happens in your cock and what happens in your biceps have a tremendous advantage; they are

❏ The origin of the word masturbate is from the Latin "manu" (hand) and "stuprare" (to defile).

routinely worked all the time. The cock isn't. The biceps are accustomed to--and designed for--hard labor. The cock has to be trained as if it were an atrophied bicep.

The aforementioned process accounts for the thickness of the cock after a vacuum pump session. Added length comes from a different set of circumstances. Inside your body there is a ligament that attaches to the corpus cavernosa--the ligament acts as a suspension cable for the shaft of the cock. The two muscles actually begin further inside the body--about four to five inches in the average person. The vacuum method loosens that ligament over time, causing an inch or two more of the internal muscles to extend.

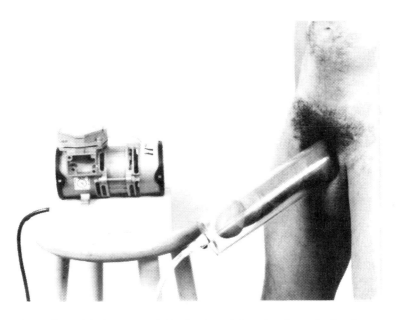

Pumping with the Dr. Joel Kaplan MegaVac electric penis developer

Ligaments are very sturdy, but not indestructible. Hence, there are limits to the stress that should be put on them. To snap the ligaments attached to the corpus cavernosum would NOT allow ALL of the rest of the muscle to extend--remember, the ligaments are a suspension device, the

---

❏　The word "homosexuality" was first coined in 1809. Before that time, it was known as "inversion" and gays were "inverts."

muscle is otherwise held in place. Ultimately, cock-building is like bodybuilding, it requires dedication, correct exercise, and time to achieve results.

Diligence and persistence are the watchwords here. While virtually all men would jump at the chance to add another inch to their penises, few are willing to invest the amount of time necessary to produce results. Champion bodybuilders dedicate years of training to produce award-winning physiques, yet when it comes to penis training, most men become highly impatient, and discontinue their efforts when they don't gain an inch in six weeks. This is folly, for successful penis developers agree that a minimum of six months (and possibly much longer) is necessary to experience noticeable increases.

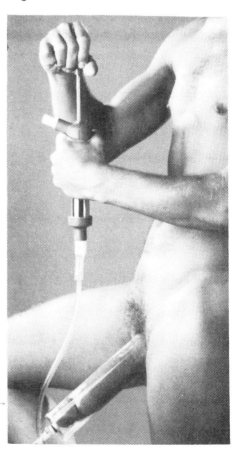

There are dozens of models of vacuum pumps on the market, but basically they can be divided into two categories--manual systems and electric systems. The manually-operated models are usually less expensive, but not always less effective. The variations are many, but the basic construction is the same. A hollow plastic or acrylic cylinder (usually 8-12" long and 2-3" in diameter) is connected to a hand pump which forces air out of the cylinder with the tug of the handle. On some of the cheaper models, the hand pump needs to be tugged constantly to maintain a satisfactory vacuum. On the better-constructed models, a tug or two on the pump is all that is required to maintain a state of full vacuum for several minutes.

Pumping with the VacuTech pump

With the electric models, the vacuum is generated by an industrial-

---

❏ What's in a name? Take the bordello district of Southware, England (near London), whose streets carry such colorful monikers as "Whore's Nest," "Slut's Hole," and "Gropecunt Lane."

110

strength electric pump which provides a consistent and steady suction. The user simply places a little lubricant around the base of the shaft to create a good seal, turns on the machine, and inserts the penis. A small valve enables the user to adjust the strength of the vacuum.

It is claimed that regular and repeated use of the pump will result in gradual and permanent enlargement. This is not the case in every individual, though. The amount of enlargement depends on several factors--the anatomy of the pumper, the regularity of use, and the length of time that the individual has pumped. The amount of time required in the penis cylinder to achieve good results varies from man to man. I have seen one man completely fill a 3" diameter chamber wall-to-wall in less than 30 minutes. It is a breathtaking sight to behold. When removed from the tube, the penis is unbelievably thick and fleshy. Most of the enlargement, however, is temporary and due primarily to lymphedema--a harmless accumulation of lymphatic fluid and lasts for perhaps a few hours, before reverting to normal size. However, one physician asserts that he experienced permanent enlargement through true vascular dilation rather than the more transitory lymphatic engorgement. We'll read his personal account shortly.

Is permanent enlargement really possible through hyperemiation? On some men, yes. Several men assert that they have gained an inch or two in length and girth. The most common question I'm asked is how long it will take to gain an inch. **"Inches"** magazine posed the same question to its readers and published the responses in the article, "Getting bigger...The Inches Guide to Penis Enlargement." Most of the respondents mentioned that they had been using their pumps for one to two years and all recorded an increase ranging from one to two inches in length. Here is a sample of the responses they received:

> Before I started to pump, my cock was 8" (20 cm) in length and 6 1/4" (16 cm) in circumference. I pump about three or four times a week. I have been pumping for a year. Now, after pumping my cock for fifteen minutes or so, the size enlarges to 9" (22 cm) in length and 7" (18 cm) in circumference. Eight hours later, and soft, my cock is still 5" (12 cm) long.

❏ In many Japanese brothels, young girls were hired for "fluting" (performing fellatio) as it was considered beneath the dignity of the geishas to engage in oral sex.

Another reader reports:

> I bought my vacuum pump two years ago and pump every other day for thirty minutes. I had a nice looking 6'' (15 cm) when I started. I have 8'' (20 cm) in length and 7'' (18 cm) in circumference. My cock is as hard as it ever was, but it feels meatier in my hand.

And yet another reader adds:

> After one year of regular pumping, I have gained almost an inch in length. What has happened faster was how thick my cock has become. I didn't measure it before, but it seems more than an inch thicker around.

Another gentleman emphasizes the increase in thickness:

> I started using (a brand name) two years ago. The main reason for me when I purchased the machine was to increase the size of my cock. Not only does it increase length but it dramatically increases thickness.

So what's the final verdict? You can count on anywhere from six months to two years to gain an inch. The time variance is dependent upon the amount of time dedicated to pumping, the type of equipment used, and the individual anatomy of the pumper. Some men show dramatic growth almost immediately. Others spend months and months, yet show little progress. The good news, however, is that virtually all men show some amount of enlargement given enough time.

Although the individuals quoted above claim appreciable increases in size, the real proof comes in the form of before and after photographs and measurements. Scientific proof notwithstanding, I know dozens of men who pump religiously, and they swear by its effectiveness. Their penises are very large and impressive. For complete details on manufacturers of vacuum pump equipment, feature-by-feature comparisons, pump clubs, and the latest research (as well as photos of veteran pumpers who have developed their penises to incredible dimensions), read *The Vacuum Pumper's Handbook*. In a study of sex aids, Dr. T. K. Peters commented on the hyperemiation method: "It is felt that this progressive exercise will strengthen and enlarge any muscle."

❏   Many of the legal brothels in Nevada greet their male customers with a "menu" of their tantalizing delights. Each sexual act has a corresponding price.

A word of caution. Care needs to be exercised when a novice starts pumping. Overzealous use can cause "petechiae," which are innocuous, red, pinprick-sized hemorrhages that occur on the glans and shaft. They are painless ruptures in the capillaries of the penis which are exacerbated by continuous vacuum. They tend to disappear within a few days. However, extended use of the vacuum will create even more petechiae and over the course of several weeks, the entire shaft will darken. Once the penis takes on the darker pigment, it will take months without pumping to return to its normal hue. Moderate and judicious usage will obviate this hyperpigmentation.

Let me briefly tell you about a machine that deserves special mention. The CTC XL1000 electric penis pulsator was designed by a mechanical engineer. The machine pulses and throbs on the penis while enlarging it more effectively than any other device I have yet tested. The machine isn't much to look at, with spartan design and deceptively simple function, but boy-oh-boy, does it work! What it lacks in looks, it more than compensates for in performance.

When I first acquired the machine for evaluation, I was quite skeptical. I unzipped my fly, withdrew my cock, greased it up, and inserted it into the clear butyrate chamber. I turned on the machine and immediately felt it take

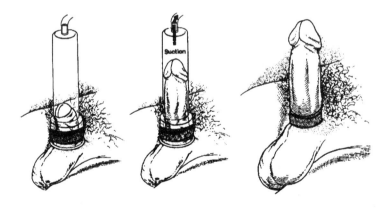

The Osbon ErecAid™ system--a medical penis pump available by prescription only

hold of my cock. What really surprised me was that it gently pulsated and throbbed at 50 beats a minute--in time with my heartbeat. This action distinguishes it from all other pumps on the market. The pulsing suck-relax-suck-relax action allows fresh blood to enter the penis, bathing the tissues with oxygen--the rich, life-giving food for blood cells. Other pumps generate a continuous vacuum which allows stagnant blood to pool in the penis. This increases the likelihood of blisters and petechiae.

Within 15 minutes, my cock had inflated to dimensions I had never seen before. When I withdrew it from the chamber, I had a hard time believing that this was my cock. I was wearing a pair of Brooks Bros. khaki trousers (they always reveal everything) and had to stop at the grocery store on the way home. My cock was still huge from the pumping session, and the sight of this beercan-thick cock hanging down my pantleg sent one married man crashing into the potato chip display with a loaded shopping cart. Another man quickly excused himself from his wife and furtively followed me around the store while I nonchalantly scanned the shelves for nutmeg.

Vacuum pumps have found a therapeutic niche in the medical field. Physicians routinely prescribe specialty pumps for their male patients who suffer from impotence. After the man inflates his penis with the vacuum chamber, the cylinder is removed and a constrictive ring is placed around the base of the penis to prohibit blood from escaping. This results in a partial erection--one that is sufficiently firm for engaging in intercourse. For complete details on the latest devices for treating impotence (implants, vacuum pumps, and injections for erections) read *Penis Power--A Complete Guide to Potency Restoration.*

A physician writes of the virtues of hyperemiation:

At my age (late 50s) it is incredible that I am beginning to have a cock like I always dreamed of! I used to be 6'' (15 cm) in length and a scant 1 1/2'' (6 cm) in diameter. Today my prick is 6 3/4'' (17 cm) in length and for at least 24 hours after an hour-long pumping session, I can maintain an almost 2'' (2.5 cm) diameter erection.

Another physician, based in Lindborg, Kansas, writes:

I really think you have given the world a very valuable machine and I am certain that if more men knew the absolutely wonderful sensations available with the use of your machine, you would be swamped with

❏ Masters & Johnson's research found that the gay men, on average, have larger penises than heterosexual men.

orders. I know that as a doctor, I recommend it unconditionally to any man who wants to discover thrills he had never imagined and also wanted to enlarge his cock.

And yet another medical doctor praises the effectiveness of the CTC XL1000:

> The CTC is like an all-new experience. I'm pleased with the results I'm getting. I'm not really sure just how much of all this is permanent, but I do know that for several hours, at least, my cock is a treasure to behold! The increase in thickness to me is the most important feature.

A reader recently wrote to me, reaffirming that patience and many months of diligence are necessary to achieve satisfactory results:

> I am sure that I've added at least 1/2'' (1.3 cm) permanently and 1/4'' (.7 cm) in circumference. Tell your readers it just takes time. I almost despaired at 6-7 months. I'm glad I kept at it.

A couple of summers ago I spent some time with a Norwegian friend at his home in suburban Oslo. A distinguished Harvard professor and international financier, he is not easily impressed. He had read my book and inquired about vacuum pumps. I happened to have one in my travel bag. We were about to embark on an afternoon excursion through the fjords in his sailboat and he encouraged me to bring the pump along. Barely 10 nautical miles out of Oslo, he suggested that we disrobe and enjoy the mid-summer

---

Penis enlargement recipe

Here is an ancient Hindu recipe for lengthening the penis:

"Take equal quantities of **Chikana** (*hedysarum lagopodioides*), **Lechi**, **Kosth** (*costus speciosus* or *arabicus*), **Verkhand** (Iris root), **Gajapimpali** (*pothos oficinalis*), **Askhand** (*physalis flexuosa*), and **Kanther-root** (oleander, *nerium odorum*); pound these and mix with butter. Apply this composition to the organ, and after about two ghari (45 minutes) it will attain the largeness of the member of a horse."

❏   You've heard of the female "G spot." Recent research shows that men have an area of equivalent sensitivity and responsiveness. It is the prostate. When properly stimulated, it can send a man into orgasmic nirvana. Gay men have known this for centuries.

sunshine. In the nude, he invited me to steer for awhile. Rolf went below into the galley and emerged with my overnight bag. "Is your pump in here?" he asked. "Yes, it's right on top," I responded. Rolf unzipped the bag and handed it to me, inviting me to show him how to use it. I returned the wheel to him and adjusted the jib as the breeze shifted slightly. I smeared a little cocoa butter around the base of the tube, inserted my penis, and gave a couple of tugs on the pump handle.

Within a few minutes, my cock began to "inflate" and fill the tube. Rolf got so excited that he began to get an erection. I told him that he should be only partially erect to use it. With this, he handed the wheel back to me, lowered himself into the water and held onto the lower rung of the ladder while the sailboat pulled him along at a swift 10 knots. When he emerged from the salty, refreshing fjord, he asked "Now am I ready?" I assured him that he was. I dried his genitals, greased the base of his cock, and placed the tube over his cock, giving the pump handle a couple of tugs. He sat down on a life preserver and watched as his Viking penis began to fill the tube. In utter amazement, he exclaimed that he had never seen his cock that big before, and frankly, I too, was surprised at how large it had become. Needless to say, I navigated for the next couple of hours while he amused himself with his new toy. Rolf has been an avid pumper ever since, and he recently invited me for a week-long trip up the Norwegian coast with two other friends. "Bring four pumps this time," he suggested with a wink and a smile.

Conclusion: The hyperemiation method really works, but it takes great dedication and time. The workouts should consist of 30-60 minute sessions (using only a moderate vacuum), conducted several times a week. For complete details on how to safely enlarge through pumping, read *The Vacuum Pumper's Handbook.*

The Arabic Jelq Method

The Sudanese Arabs possess some of the largest penises in the world. Although born with average-sized phalli, from the onset of adolescence, the males are initiated into an age-old practice passed down from father to son. Around age 8, the father instructs his son to grasp the root of the penis with thumb and forefinger and stroke from the bottom to the top to initiate the

---

❏   Tao philosophy claims that there are specific reflexology points (meridians) on the penis that correspond to different organs of the body. By massaging these specific points through masturbation, one can bring energy to these organs.

lengthening process. The youth is encouraged to do this for 30 minutes each day, taking special precautions not to ejaculate. If the boy senses that orgasm is quickly approaching, he stops, waits for the sensation to subside, then resumes the procedure.

In more affluent families, the father may send his son to a "mehbil," the Arabic equivalent of our athletic club. A highly-trained attendant administers to the boy, performing the "jelq" on a daily basis. The boy is stripped and vigorously massaged with a pungent patchouli-scented oil. His penis is then skillfully manipulated with a "milking" motion by the attendant. The boy is instructed not to ejaculate. When the attendant senses that the boy is reaching ejaculatory inevitability, the massage is halted, and then resumed. Orgasm is approached (but not completed) six or seven times each session. Holding back is an exercise in restraint which instills a sense of self-control in his marital relations. More importantly, though, the massage stimulates circulation in the genitalia and the increased blood supply is momentarily trapped in the corpora cavernosa.

Over a period of months, the blood spaces in the penis are gradually enlarged through repeated and sustained vascular dilation and become capable of accepting more blood. The Sudanese Arabs know that this is particularly effective when the procedure is initiated in puberty, just when the youth's penis is beginning to grow (a boy reaches his maximum penis size at around age 17). These exercises can truly encourage growth far beyond that which the penis normally would have attained. Had each of us initiated such a program during adolescence, no doubt we would all be hung like horses.

Although this method works best on young men who have not yet reached their full phallic development, it works on adults as well. A few years ago, a gay magazine ran a story about a body builder who was self-conscious about his small penis. His trainer was an Arab who had previously worked as a mehbil. The body builder allegedly was able to develop a truly mammoth penis, measuring some 11" (27 cm) in length. As I have not seen before and after photos of this man, I cannot vouch for its authenticity. Here is an excerpt from the article:

> Into a quart-size jar of mayonnaise, stir a heaping tablespoon of white or yellow corn meal. Mix it well. Now protect your hair with a rubber bath cap and apply the mixture liberally, beginning with your face and neck. Then coat your chest, arms, and back...work down until

---

❑ One sex act which has gained in popularity with the rise of safe sex is "docking" in which the foreskin of one man is drawn up over the glans of his male partner. Both penises are then masturbated simultaneously.

even your feet and toes are covered. Then...turn your shower on "hot' and while the steam surrounds you, tub the mixture well into your skin...then after a few minutes of steam, turn the shower to "warm," step under and rinse yourself well. Soap? Forget it.

Right away you will experience a tingling glow. The skin soon acquires a very beautiful, rich, satiny finish from these treatments...Next, lie on the bed...and begin the stimulation phase. I do this every day when possible, certainly never fewer than five days a week because I found that the more "workout" days I put in, the larger and faster it grew.

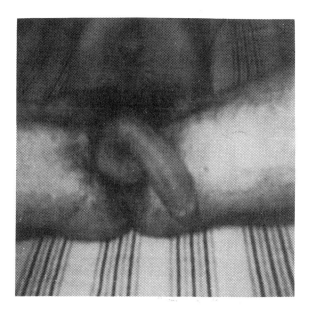

This Scottish man added an inch to his penis through the "Jelq" method

Heeding my friend's advice, I performed the ritual slowly, using long strokes with 1 or 2 fingers--never the closed hand--and worked up to near climax at least six times during each stimulation ritual. At first I found this difficult because with each period of stimulation, the tendency to ejaculate was almost overpowering. However, by gauging the 'nearness point' I was able to avoid it by stopping in time. Then I would relax and allow the penis to become semi-erect, and I

❑   Among the Keraki tribe of New Guinea, all pubescent boys are expected to submit to anal and oral sex for a year. The Keraki believe that the semen received from older, mature males will enable them to develop into strong, healthy men. Failure to do so will leave them small, weak, and inferior.

118

continued with the second and other stimulations. Sometimes a feeling of frustration occurred around the fifth or sixth stage of stimulation, and when this happened, I allow the ejaculation, ending the ritual at that point.

A couple of years ago, I received a letter and photo from a reader in Scotland who underwent a Jelq-like procedure. In his words:

> I received a copy of your book in November, I found it very interesting. I then decided to try the Arabic Jelq method. To my amazement, my cock has increased in length and girth, so much so, my affair has noticed the difference as well. I enclosed a photo you can keep.

The photo he submitted (next page) shows a truly impressive member. He claims to have started with an organ measuring 6 1/2" (16.5 cm) in length by 4 3/4" (12 cm) in girth and ending at 7 1/2" (19 cm) by 5 1/2" (14 cm). In a more recent follow-up letter he added more details about his procedure:

> My workout sessions last about 20 minutes per day. I only use the milking method as that was the only way my friend taught me. I noticed a significant change after about 4 weeks. I gained my first full inch after about 16-18 weeks. From the time I started the exercise to the time I reached 7 1/2'' was about 22-24 weeks give or take a week or two.

A gentleman in Northern California wrote, telling me that he had learned the method from his Turkish father. He provided some fascinating insights into the particulars of Jelq:

> My father, being a Turk, introduced me to the method called çelik (pronounced chaylick) when I was starting puberty at 11 years old and I still practice it. It takes some practice, but it's also fun to do when one has idle hours. Being a father myself, I showed my own son how to do it, but he doesn't need it really since the genes from his mother's side of the family had already 'blessed' him so to speak. Basically, it is the same thing as the 'Jelq' method from what you have written. Turks picked up several habits from the Arabs and have retained them, being mostly Moslem, although Jewish Turks employ the same techniques.
>
> I was only eight or nine at the time. I never saw my own father's penis before the little operation. I was tugging on it one day in my

---

❏ The Japanese have developed a dildo that actually expels a semen-like fluid.

119

bedroom when he walked in. He pulled his big thing out and I gasped at the size of it. He told me that mine would be as big if I did çelik. So that was when I learned. As I got older, I did it every day. My father did learn this method from my grandfather, as did he from his own father. The purpose is quite simple--penile enlargement and personal pleasure.

He explains that the procedure involves a concerted "milking" of the shaft to increase the engorgement of the shaft. The penis should not be completely erect. When the man feels that he is approaching orgasm, he backs off, and only resumes when the feeling of ejaculatory inevitability subsides. This masturbatory exercise is continued for at least 30 minutes a day, and orgasm is allowed only after ejaculation has been approached 6-7 times.

In July of 1994 I received a letter from a reader in Oregon who learned "jelq" from his family. "Peter" was born in the Azores--a collection of vulcanic islands in the North Atlantic that belong to Portugal. When he was 11 or 12, shortly before emigrating to the U.S., his paternal grandfather entered his bedroom and instructed him in the art of phallic massage which he claimed would help strengthen and elongate the penis. He didn't have a name for the procedure, but said that he learned it from his own grandfather, who was Moroccan. Every male in his family learned this penile massage, and most of the men engaged in it on a daily basis. "Peter" provided me with distinct and specific details on the execution of the 3-4 exercises involved. They corresponded nearly identically to the exercises described by Scott.

Conclusion: The heart of Jelq/Çelik involves a prolonged masturbation using slow and deliberate hand-over-hand milking motions to increase the amount of blood to the penis. Another component involves massaging the perineum where the "crura" or root of the penis is located (between the scrotum and the anus). Although it is usually initiated in childhood in Middle Eastern countries, adult men may find success with it as well, however, a minimum of a year is required to see real results. Complete instructions to this unique phallic massage can be found in *Penis Power Quarterly*. My new video, *Gary Griffin's Guide to Better Pumping* ($29.95 from Added Dimensions Publishing) also explicitly demonstrates the technique.

❏ Dr. Gabriello Fallopius, who developed the modern condom a couple of centuries back, advised parents to be diligent in enlarging the penises of their newborn sons. Just what his recipe is for enlarging is not mentioned.

Constriction therapy

This is more of a maintenance therapy for men undergoing penis enlargement programs rather than an enlargement technique in itself. It involves constricting the base of the penis with a band or ring. The ring may be made of metal, rubber, or plastic, and its purpose is to keep the penis engorged for a longer period of time, thereby completely distending and expanding the blood spaces in the corpora cavernosa.

Caution needs to be exercised when using a ring of metal or plastic as they are inflexible and can cause strangulation of the penis if not removed in time. Medical journals abound with tales of foolhardy men who carelessly slip a wedding ring or other small object around the penis. When erection occurs, blood enters and is incapable of escaping. The pain can be excruciating and the object must frequently be removed with a surgical saw. Ouch!!

The only ring I recommend for this purpose is the "Stallion cock cushion" manufactured by CTC Company. The ring comes in five different models, varying in degrees of constriction. The loosest is stretchable like a thick rubber band, while the tightest is more rigid and provides the greatest constriction. "Stallion cock cushions" (around $17 apiece) measure 1" in width and 1/4" in thickness and are designed to be worn around the base of the penis. The resulting constriction allows the penis to hang out at its maximum flaccid dimensions. I have not found a more effective device for keeping the penis hanging long and thick while flaccid. If you want to show an impressive "basket" under clothing, "Stallion Cock Cushions" are the key.

Conclusion: The constriction method by itself may not provide permanent enlargement, but when used as an adjunct to the hyperemiation or milking methods, the results can be quite striking. For a brochure describing the "Stallion Cock Cushions," contact: CTC Company, P.O. Box 2517, Van Nuys, CA, 91404.

10-1-97

❏ Natives of the Trobriand Islands are among the most sexually-liberated on earth. Children are allowed to participate in sex at an early age, and all forms of sexual experimentation are considered acceptable. Children and adults alike are allowed free expression of their sexual desires.

Blakoe Ring

Not truly a penis enlargement device in itself, the Blakoe Ring is an intriguing support apparatus that claims to aid the wearer in achieving greater potency and larger, stiffer erections. The ring was invented by Dr. Blakoe over 50 years ago and boasts a large and loyal following of satisfied users in Europe. Constructed of black ebonite, the ring is designed to fit around both the penis

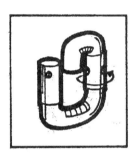 

and testicles. It is a rounded rectangular shape with hinges that allow it to open like a combination lock. The top portion swivels to permit the wearer to put it on easily and comfortably. The inner area of the top and bottom portions are inlaid with copper plates. These act as thermocouples that produce minute, yet detectible electrical currents generated by the heat of the body and are said to stimulate the flow of blood to the genitalia and even generate a greater flow of testosterone.

The *British Journal of Psychiatry* and *Medical Digest* contain physician endorsements of the Blakoe Ring. One doctor writes:

> After using the Blakoe Ring for 3 weeks (one patient) noticed that erections were 40-50% more rigid. His frequency of intercourse increased from 3-4 times per month to 8 per month and there was a definite increase in the diameter of the penis. In repose it was generally larger and showed increased muscle tone.

Dr. Robert Chartham reported in *Forum:*

> All, including myself, have noted that while the ring is being worn, the penis remains constantly at its maximum flaccid dimensions.

It is debatable whether the minute electrical charges generated by the ring truly increase the flow of testosterone. The beneficial effects are probably both psychological and physical. The ring does constrict the penis and testicles to a slight degree, providing more powerful erections.

❑ Indian natives of Patagonia place a ring of coarse mule hair around the base of the penis before sex. Known as a "guesquel," it is said to act as a clitoral stimulator, resulting in intense female orgasms.

Conclusion: While the Blakoe Ring may not contribute to a permanent increase in penis size, it will assist in maintaining a powerful erection and may even increase the output of testosterone. Wearing the ring can be quite erotic and pleasurable. While not for everyone, the Blakoe Ring makes a novel addition to any man's sexual armamentarium. For a brochure, write: Dipix Distributions, P.O. Box 75, Sandwich, Kent, CT13 9RT, Great Britain.

10-1-97

SE 101

Also known as the **"Dr. Taylor 16 week natural penis development plan,"** this method incorporates mental imagery, massage, and acupressure. Their introductory brochure says that this method was developed by a young Ph.D. in philosophy who wanted to know why the genetic code had a particular timing connected to hormone production. Specifically, he wanted to find out why hormone production couldn't be stimulated to continue past puberty, thereby enabling the penis to continue to grow.

This curiosity led him to medical research libraries to better understand the mysteries of endocrinology and later to a set of obscure Oriental volumes that explored sexual secrets from India, Tibet, and China. What he concluded was that by combining modern scientific knowledge with ancient methods of acupressure and reflex stimulation, the genetic code could be altered, causing growth to continue as long as the reflexes were stimulated. In fact, he claims that "growth could be made to go on endlessly--and safely."

Once he had developed his protocol, Dr. Taylor secured a group of Hong Kong males to try out the system. At the conclusion of the trial, he claimed a 95% success rate in enlarging the penises of the men in this group. What is incredible is his assertion that one "must be warned...to set limits to growth before you order the program." He states that one man in Hong Kong became so obsessed with size that he developed a donkey-sized penis measuring 30 (count 'em--THIRTY) inches (75 cm) in length by 2 1/2" (5 cm) in diameter, with a head as big as a man's fist. He allegedly started out with an erection measuring 5" (12.5 cm) long by 1" (2.5 cm) in diameter. This man now supposedly makes his living dancing in Hong Kong and Bangkok nightclubs where tourists pay big bucks to watch him prance

---

❑ In many Oceanic and Asian cultures, a psychological phenomenon known as "Koro" exists--an irrational fear that the male's penis is shrinking and disappearing into the abdomen.

around nude while scantily-clad females fondle and lick his organ. *(Readers note: I lived in Bangkok for several years and never heard of such an individual. If one did indeed exist, wouldn't word certainly have traveled around the globe? Wouldn't he have become an underground legend by now? After all, even John Holmes and Long Dong Silver have become household names, but this is the first time I have ever heard of such an Asian male--who allegedly is TWICE as long as the legendary Long Dong. Besides, a 30" penis would drag on the ground--therefore I have serious doubts about this claim and will have to be shown photographs before believing).*

This enlargement course sells for $25 and consists of a poorly reproduced instruction booklet peppered with typographical errors--further detracting from its credibility. Dr. Taylor says that the growth of the sex organs is encouraged by stimulating the natural growth mechanism "by contacting a group of accu-pressure (sic) points which were until now, a closely-guarded secret among monks studying TANTRA meditation--a form of worship through sexual union known among Hindu's (sic), Buddhists, and Tauists (sic) of India, Tibet, and China." The course consists of the following:

❏ **Mental imagery using self-hypnotic suggestion and image picture holding**

During self-hypnosis, the brain is induced to release specific chemicals and hormones to stimulate the enlargement process. Every night before retiring, the man is instructed to visualize his body with a larger penis. The stronger the mental image, the more they claim the nervous response will make this a reality. This is done for 5-10 minutes each evening.

❏ **Contacting reflex points and acupressure points with the hands and "electromagnetic antennae" made of common copper beebees which are taped in place.**

A special chart included in the program shows where to place the beebees to encourage growth. Some points are stimulated to promote thickness, some for growth of the glans, and others for the testicles. These are worn all day until retiring for bed. They are removed for sleep and replaced upon arising.

❏ **Diet and exercise**
❏ **Massages to encourage "nervous system awakening contact."**

The "CX-6" meridians (specific acupressure points on the body) are rubbed in small quick circles for about a minute each upon arising in the morning

---

❏ Until 1980, the world's most sophisticated sexual device was manufactured. The "AccuJac" was an automatic masturbator with controls for suction strength, stroke length, and stroke rapidity. The author is the proud owner of the deluxe AccuJac II with six different sized penis sleeves.

and again before retiring at night. These spots allegedly stimulate the lymphatic and vascular systems to carry nutrients to the related organs while removing waste products. An ancillary massage involves applying a lubricant and milking the cock from base to tip to push blood into the shaft and head. This is performed for 10 minutes a day.

Conclusion: The method certainly sounds intriguing, and many of the points described (mental imagery, milking exercises) certainly have their place in any penis enlargement program. Whether or not the stimulation of the acupressure points contributes to enlargement is up to question. What concerns the author is the claim that these are closely-held secrets of the Indians, Chinese, and Tibetans. Curiously, these are among the most modestly-endowed races in the world. If these methods worked, certainly, we'd find hordes of endowed Asians. A method previously mentioned in this chapter describes Tibetan Monks who have developed equine phalli, so perhaps there are some Asians who have derived benefit from it. I express some doubt simply because I have seen no visual proof of endowed Asian males let alone anyone else who has experienced enlargement through this course. Several of my *Penis Power Quarterly* readers attempted the course themselves, but none reported enlargement. I am NOT saying that it doesn't work. The material I received, while interesting, consisted of a stapled, xeroxed booklet replete with misspelled words and grammatical lapses. Any "doctor" with a bonafide education would certainly not be guilty of such an obvious academic solecism.

The Campo Method

In the 1980s, peripatetic, self-proclaimed "metaphysician" (whatever that is) Dr. C. Ralph Campo offered a penis enlargement enlargement to those willing to part with $25. What I received in return for my money was a jumbled, incohesive potpourri of xeroxed material that was difficult to understand and even harder to logically accept. Dr. Campo claims that he is one of the ten best psychics in the U.S. in addition to being a "clairvoyant, medium, psychic healer, and advisor to executives and movie greats." Just what kind of doctor Mr. Campo really is, is anybody's guess.

His course consists of the following:

❏   There is no relationship between the size of the penis and the size of the testicles.

- ❏ Isometric contractions
- ❏ Acupressure contact points
- ❏ Breathing exercises to charge the psychic energy
- ❏ Magnetization of water
- ❏ Self conditioning session "in the alpha state of mind to build new subconscious patterns"

Does the face reveal penis size?

According to Stephen T. Chang, M.D., facial clues (physiognomy) provide unique insights into the size and shape of your penis. A physician and Eastern religion scholar, Dr. Chang states that in Tao theory, the face reveals everything. By learning the specific techniques of facial analysis, one can determine a person's complete personality. Other physical characteristics give clues as to the length and shape of a man's organ. According to Dr. Chang, these clues are about 90% accurate:

- ❏ A man with a long nose and long fingers will have a long penis.
- ❏ A man with a short nose and short fingers will have a short penis.
- ❏ A man with a long nose and short fingers, or a short nose and long fingers, will have a medium-length penis.
- ❏ If the tip of the nose is fat, he will have a fat penis. Likewise a thin tip will signal a thin penis.
- ❏ The thumb is shaped like the penis. If the thumb is "mushroom" shaped, the penis will have a large head and a narrow shaft. If the thumb is "triangular" in shape, the penis will reflect this shape.
- ❏ Thick, wide lips signal a large penis.

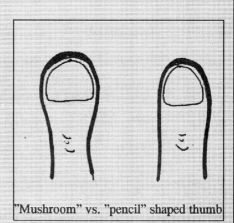

"Mushroom" vs. "pencil" shaped thumb

- ❏ Foot-long penises. Just how common are they? According to current statistical models, there are less than 1,000 12" (30 cm.) penises in the entire world.

The first step consists of performing "buttock contractions" (actually "Kegel exercises") which are the rhythmic contraction of the pubococcygeal muscle--the same one you use to stop the flow of urine. The second phase involves the application of pressure against specific points in the neck, feet, legs, groin, perineum, and chest. Breathing exercises are taught to help focus one's energy. The "magnetization of water" is needless hocus pocus.

His instruction manual says that "everything is very simple to follow." Understanding nuclear fission is easy compared to this manual. The booklet is so cluttered, incohesive, and replete with spelling errors that the reader is left scratching his head in wonderment. Xeroxed photos of well-endowed models clipped from old gay magazines are used as examples, but curiously, none are provided from men who actually completed the course.

Conclusion: This course is representative of the sleazy, tawdry courses offered in the back of men's magazines. This is not to say that the course is not without merit. Indeed, visualization, penile manipulation, and isometric contractions of the pubococcygeal muscle are all beyond reproach. However, when so-called "doctors" with dubious degrees expound on bizarre, cosmic concepts such as "water magnetization" and "alpha wave conditioning," then I have problems. Dr. Campo lists several different addresses in his material--National City, San Diego, Los Angeles, Yuma, and Bullhead City. Is he running from something? If the material were presented in a logical, understandable, easy-to-follow format complete with case studies and before and after photographs, then it would be accepted with greater credence.

The "V" Method

Several years ago, New Jersey resident Eugene Viscione developed an intractable case of "Peyronie's Disease" (an abnormal curvature of the penis). This syndrome can develop at any time in life and is usually attributed to penile trauma, especially during sex. Imagine that you're thrusting into your partner with gusto. On the outstroke, your penis slips out. As you drill it back in you miss the hole and come down heavily on your partner's pelvis. This can literally "break" the penis and the resulting scarring can cause the organ to bend to the right, to the left, up, or down. If the curvature is severe, it can cause painful erections and may make intercourse impossible.

❏ In the Ivory Coast, the natives apparently use an herb called "Kushumit" for enlarging the penis.

All "cures" for Peyronie's disease are either experimental or anecdotal. Many times, the condition resolves spontaneously without further action. Other men opt for surgery, in which a nick is taken out of the opposite side of the scar to straighten the penis out. This can shorten the penis, however, and there is no guarantee that the condition won't return.

Mr. Viscione's vexing curvature (he provides photos for proof) caused his erection to shrink several inches. His doctors were at a loss as to how to treat his case. Surgery was out of the question, lest he lose even more length. In the face of this obstacle, he began experimenting with penile manipulation in an attempt to dissolve the scar tissue and straighten the shaft. The result was a series of specific penile massages using nothing more than mineral oil and vitamin E. Mr. Viscione claims that he not only straightened out his penis, but he gained in both length and girth. Although this all sounds incredible, he provides photos showing his severely bent penis (before) and the newly-enlarged straightened organ (after). Personal letters from several physicians also attest to his pre- and post-Peyronie's condition. The "V" Method consists of a booklet ($15) and an optional video. For more information, write to: P.O. Box 416, Somerville, NJ 08876.

Conclusion: Many of the exercises presented in the "V" method are similar to the milking exercises mentioned previously. These do have benefit to the vascularity of the penis, and although the author is not totally convinced that genuine enlargement is achieved through this method, the exercises certainly will help keep the penis distended at its maximim flaccid dimensions. Also, for men with Peyronie's disease, this method is to be recommended as a first or last therapy for penile curvature.

❏ For those men who want to show a "basket" but lack the large equipment they'd like, Renard Industries has developed a brief with a detachable cloth dildo that looks impressive under clothing. Call (800) 225-1670 for more information.

Project P

In early 1994, I received a letter from a gentleman in South Africa who claimed to have developed a unique protocol for increasing the size of the penis. In my years of research, I had heard this many times before, so was understandably skeptical. Yet there was something about his sincerity which intrigued me enough to investigate further.

During the next few months, the developer of the program, Wilhelm Lötter and I carried on a lively intercontinental correpondence via fax. Several hundred men in his country had participated in his regimen (which he named "Project P") and he provided several unsolicited letters from satisfied men as proof of their gain in penis size. Word about this unique program swept through South Africa, landing him on the covers of several magazines with the headline "This man can turn your willy into a whopper!" Since that time, his phone has been ringing off the hook and mail is now delivered by the sackful.

As a researcher, I've been trained to never accept allegations on face value, so I asked if I might conduct trials of my own. In the July 1994 issue of *Penis Power Quarterly* I requested a dozen volunteers to participate in a three month trial of "Project P." To my amazement, I received over 200 requests to participate. Due to the overwhelming response, I expanded the participant base to 75 individuals, including 6 physicians and the trials began in August, 1994 and concluded in November.

The course consists of 6 exercises which must be performed 15-20 minutes daily for a period of three months. Mr. Lötter claims that one can expect increases of 2-8 cm. (1-3").

Conclusion: The preliminary results to the trial have been disappointing. Only a handful of the participants experienced any growth whatsoever. When I told Mr. Lötter, he was very surprised, claiming that South African men have had great success. He suspected the participants may have done the exercises incorrectly, so he sent a video explicitly demonstrating the steps. I've invited my readers to get a copy of the video from me ($20) and try again. Further developments will be reported in *Penis Power Quarterly.*

❑   According to the **"British Medical Journal"** 19% of British men found standard condoms too tight.

Underground German experiment

The following is one of the most intriguing stories I've ever encountered. It sounds too incredible to be true, but several factors lead me to believe that there there may be something to it. One of my close friends has come across 3-4 men who mysteriously increased the size of their penis over a period of time. Each one of these young men were "kept" as lovers by successful gay businessmen.

During the time of their romance, these young men were taken to Europe for several months. Upon returning, their penises had suddenly grown a couple of inches. To date, each one of these men (now in their 30s and 40s) remains mum on the subject and we suspect that they are under an oath of secrecy--and understandably so. After all, if the news of a successful penis enlargement program got out to the mainstream, then every man would have access to a 10" penis. This, of course, would then obviate the phallic advantage and "specialness" of the original enlargers. For this reason, they obviously want to keep it quiet and available only to a select cadre of men.

To support my suspicions that there may indeed be a subrosa European clinic for increasing the size of the penis, I came across an article in the *Bay Area Reporter* which reported the following story by an eavesdropping student attending UC San Francisco:

> "While eating lunch at the cafeteria, my attention was drawn to the word 'cock' being spoken at the table behind me. The two men were engrossed in a discussion as they finished their meals. I confess to eavesdropping on as much of the rest of their conversation as I could make out above the noise. What I heard was fascinating.

> "Scientists in Germany last year were said to have discovered a 'growth factor' responsible for the increase in penis size that boys experience at puberty. When the researchers administered this substance to several adult volunteers they found that it caused further cock size increases. The nature of this cock growth factor wasn't clear to me, but the speaker said it had 'an unfortunate side-effect.' The subjects lost interest in females and developed an attraction to males. Afraid of a public outcry, the research director encouraged everyone involved in the experiment to keep mum about it.

"By this time, of course, I was shamelessly straining to hear every word of this amazing story. And it got even better. Since the growth factor, when used by adults, caused both penis enlargement and homosexual inclincations, the researchers reasoned that the same might be true in adolescent boys. If so, then there out to be a correlation between sexual orientation and final cock size. (Reader note: Masters and Johnsons did indeed confirm that homosexuals on average, sport larger penises than heterosexuals, although no explanation for this anomaly is available).

Noise interfered with my eavesdropping effort for a time, and when it quited down, the conversation concerned what was apparently a follow-up study involving several dozen men. No growth factor was administered in this study. A physician and a psychologist determined the penis length and sexual orientation of each subject. It was found that homosexual men's cock are, on the average, more than a centimeter (.4") longer than those of heterosexual men. The likely explanation for this result is that homosexual adolescents are better endowed with cock growth factor than their heterosexual counterparts.

❏   Before going into battle, a Maori warrior crawls between the legs of a powerful chief, believing that his penis will shed strength on him.

The Chartham method

In the early 1970s, the author and sex counselor, Robert Chartham, developed this method in the face of much criticism and opposition. Dr. Chartham and associates explored every known method of penis enlargement, no matter how ridiculous. There were mechanical devices, suction gadgets, herbs, creams, potions, and stretching machines. Each of these was considered, and tested for efficacy where possible. The result was a complete program of penis development which incorporated those methods which proved to have some positive effect in enlarging the penis.

The medical basis of the Chartham method centers around the physiological fact that if a body muscle is repeatedly and thoroughly used, it has a tendency to enlarge. Researchers in the Cook islands discovered women who developed outsized clitoridae through daily manipulation. Back in 1902, Drs. White and Martin, in their medical textbook, noted "uncommonly-developed" penises of tremendous size among imbeciles and other congenitally-defective men who were chronic and habitual masturbators. Along this same line, researchers at Tulane University in New Orleans showed that the genitals of male rats atrophied when deprived of sexual activity. This seems to show that deliberate and repeated manipulation can encourage enlargement over a period of time. Such is the principle involved with body building, in which muscles that are exercised repeatedly with weights undergo a process known as hypertrophy. These muscles actually increase in size, strength, and endurance. Consequently, there is no reason why the penis, which is also composed of muscular and vascular tissues (although the penis is not itself a muscle, it is composed of smooth muscle and fibro-muscular tissue), should not be capable of enlargement as well.

Since the program was first introduced in 1975, the course has been used by thousands of men in Europe, and more recently, in America. For those who are interested in pursuing the course, the specific regimen is provided. I purchased the course in 1985 and diligently followed the regimen for a period of 8 months. My penis, in full erection at the start of the course, measured 6 1/4" (16 cm) in length by 5 1/2" (14 cm) in circumference. At the end of the course, my penis measured 7 1/2" (19 cm) in length by 6 1/4" (16 cm) in circumference, which, according to the penis size distribution curve (presented earlier), now places me in the upper 15%.

❏   The most common sexual activity among heterosexual couples is vaginal intercourse. Among homosexual couples, it is fellatio (oral sex).

In the original instructions, it is mentioned that the Chartham method takes 100 days. I find this to be grossly misleading. Of the hundreds of readers who have followed this penis enlargement course under my supervision, permanent enlargement occurs at a much slower pace. In fact, while most men notice temporary gains almost immediately, the permanent gains may not become apparent for six months or so. This agonizingly slow development is the single greatest reason why men abandon the course. Most men expect to see an inch magically appear over the space of six weeks. Sorry fellows, it just isn't going to happen that quickly.

There are five sections to the program:

❏ **Exercises**
❏ **Hot compresses**
❏ **Sensation-heightening procedures**
❏ **Penile massage**
❏ **Vacuum suction**

The instructions provided below eliminate some of the steps which the author feels do not directly contribute to enlargement. To make the course easier, the steps have been pared down to three rather than the five mentioned above. The exercises must be performed every day, unless, of course, illness or injury makes this impossible. The success of each day's progress is predicated upon the exercises conducted during previous days.

When Dr. Chartham completed the protocol for his program, he conducted a full-scale medical trial in a private clinic in Kent, England to verify its effectiveness and practicality. Physicians in this clinic recruited patients who demonstrated an interest in enlargement. Those with a chronic disease, who had non-cooperative spouses, or who had previously participated in a penis-enlargement program were excluded from the study. Finally, a group of 64 men was selected. These men were divided into two groups--the study participants and the control group. The length and circumference of each participant's penis was measured weekly by the same technician for the three month duration of the course. Of the 32 men who enrolled in the enlargement protocol, 30 completed the course. And of those 30, 28 demonstrated permanent and verifiable enlargement. The concluding statistics show:

❏   A recent survey conducted about prostitution showed that oral sex is the most requested activity of both female and male prostitutes.

❑ 87.5% demonstrated enlargement

❑ The average increase in length was 1 1/8'' (2.8 cm)

❑ The average increase in circumference was 1'' (2.5 cm)

❑ The smallest increase in length was 1'' (2.5 cm)

❑ The greatest increase in length was 1 1/2'' (4 cm)

❑ The smallest increase in circumference was 7/8'' (2.2 cm)

❑ The largest increase in circumference was 1 1/4'' (3 cm)

Once the results were compiled, the details of the study were sent to the *British Journal of Sexual Medicine, Lancet,* and *The British Medical Journal.* Dick Richards, M.D., author of *The Penis,* calls the Chartham method "far and away the best method of penis enlargement that I have ever encountered."

Several points of interest emerge from this study. At the outset of the trials, 100% of the men (even those with the largest penises to begin with) expressed a desire for a larger penis. When asked whether they would prefer an increase in length or girth, 28 of the 32 opted for added length. In contrast, 16 of the 32 spouses preferred greater thickness. At the conclusion of the trial, both had their wishes fulfilled.

Now, you may look at the results and say, "Big deal, an increase of only 1" is insignificant." Not so. If we were to juxtapose an average penis measuring 6" (15 cm) in length by 6" (15 cm) in circumference next to a size 7" (18 cm) x 7" (18 cm), the difference would be astoundingly apparent. To demonstrate what a difference an inch can make, I've assembled a "march of cocks" at the end of the book, starting with a photograph of an average 6" (15 cm) cock followed by a 7" (18 cm) , 8" (20 cm), 9" (22 cm) and a whopping horse-sized 10-incher (25 cm). Take a look and you'll see what a difference an inch can make.

___

❑ The U.S. has the highest level of teenage pregnancy in the developed world. Ironically, the Netherlands, with its open sexuality, legalized prostitution, and liberal attitudes--has the lowest level.

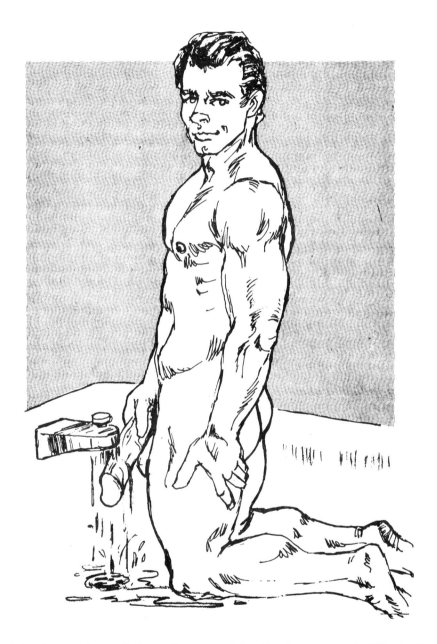

Applying heat to the penis is the first step of the Chartham protocol. This can be done by either applying hot compresses or kneeling in a tub with the penis placed under a stream of very warm water for several minutes.

135

The Chartham protocol

1) Hot compresses

The purpose of this step is to increase the blood circulation to the penis. This is accomplished by applying hot compresses to the organ. Fill a washbasin with comfortably hot water. Soak a couple of washcloths. Gently wring out the first one and wrap it around the penis and testicles. As it cools, replace it in the basin, remove the other washcloth, wring it out and apply it like the first one. You'll want to do this for 5-10 minutes. At the end of this phase, the penis will appear pink, fleshy, and slightly swollen. This is the desired result. Dry off and you're ready for step #2.

You may be wondering if all of this fuss over hot water soaks is really necessary. A study published in 1987 at the University of California, Berkeley, concluded that heat increases the blood flow to subcutaneous tissues by 3-4 times, and the oxygen supply is proportionately increased. It is this increased circulation which is necessary to exapand the corpora cavernosa (the twin spongy erectile bodies in the penis).

2) Genital Massage

In this phase, you'll notice that we concentrate not only on the penis, but on the testicles as well. The testicles are a highly responsive and erotic pair of glands that not only produce sperm cells, but also manufacture the virilizing hormone, testosterone. Massaging these organs increases circulation and encourages the production of these hormones.

A) With thumb and forefinger, perform a series of "pinches" over the entire surface area of the scrotum. Do NOT pinch the testicle itself, only the sac. As you pinch a particular area, grip it firmly and pull as far out as comfortably possible. Maintain the tension and hold for a count of five, release, and let the scrotum sping back under its own elasticity. Go on to the next area and repeat. Perform this exercise 10 times over different areas of the scrotum. Total time: 2-3 minutes.

B) Cup your left hand and cradle the testicles. Using the fingertips of your right hand, firmly but gently massage the testicles and the scrotal contents for 30 seconds. Switch hands and perform the same massage

---

❏ A recent survey conducted in the U.S. found that American women perceived circumcised penises to be sexier and more desirable. Conversely, in Europe, where circumcision is rare, many women view the uncircumcised penis in a more favorable light.

136

with the fingers of the left hand. Be careful not to apply more pressure to the testicles than you can comfortably enjoy. Total time: 1 minute.

C) Now, simultaneously massage the left testicle with the left hand and the right testicle with the right hand. A gentle pulling, rolling, and kneading motion will help stimulate the blood flow as well as encourage the production of essential male hormones. Total time: 1 minute.

D) Apply a liberal slathering of your favorite lubricant (cold cream, lotion, Vaseline®, oil) to the shaft of the penis. Make a circle with the thumb and forefinger of the right hand and grasp the shaft at the base of the penis where it joins the body. Squeeze firmly and you will feel the trapped blood in the shaft cause the penis to swell. Release and repeat the same grasping and squeezing motion over different parts of the shaft. Each time, squeeze hard for 3-5 seconds, release and move on to the next part. These squeezes force blood into the sponge-like sinuses of the corpora cavernosa. Over time, this helps enlarge these spaces, making them capable of accepting and retaining more blood. The amount of pressure you use should not cause discomfort. Total time: 1-2 minutes.

E) If your penis needs more lubrication, add it now. As above, make a circle with your thumb and forefinger and grip the shaft of the penis at the base. Applying firm and steady pressure, move your fist toward the head of your penis. Pretend you are "milking" the penis. Before your right hand reaches the end of the penis, begin the same movement with your left hand. As one hand reaches the end of the penis, it slides off and returns to repeat the same motion while the other fist is still milking the shaft. Each milking stroke should take 3-4 seconds. If you perform this step correctly, you will see and feel the end of the penis swell with increased pressure as blood is forced into the spongy spaces. This is one of the most important steps of the entire program, and is performed in a "hand-over-hand" motion. Start with 20 milking motions and increase to 100-150 repetitions by the second week. Total time: 5-10 minutes.

Note: Ideally, the penis should be semi-erect during these exercises. A rigid, fully erect penis will not respond to the exercises. Neither will a floppy, flaccid organ. A partial "hard-on" is what you're aiming for. If your penis becomes erect, you can either masturbate to ejaculation, or wait until the erection subsides somewhat before resuming.

❑ There is an underground support group for men with very small penises (approximately 10% of the population). For more information, contact: "Small, Etc.", P.O. Box 294, Bayside, NY 11361. A yearly subscription to their newsletter "The Small Gazette" is $25 ($40 outside of the U.S.).

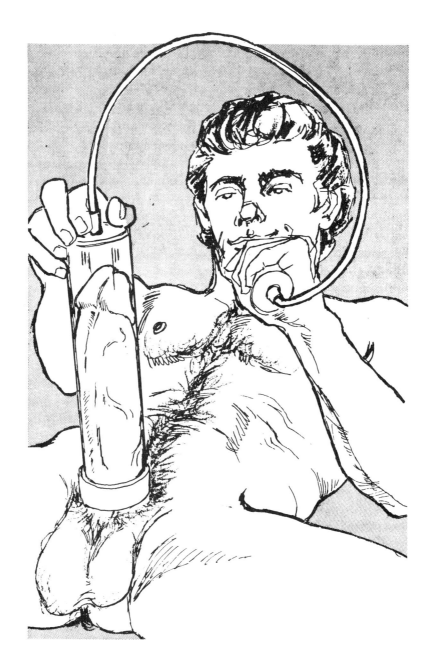

Vacuum pumping (hyperemiation) is an important component of the Chartham program.

3) Vacuum pumping

You will need to secure a high-grade penis pump for this phase. There are six models that I recommend for penis enlargement:

1) Vacu Tech pump (editor's choice)

2) San Francisco Pump Works pump

3) Dr. Joel Kaplan Mega Pump

4) Northwest Pump Works pump

5) Boston Pump Works pump

6) CTC StudMaker

The first five models come in more than a dozen sizes and feature an airlock release valve which enables you to disconnect the pump from the penis cylinder while maintaining full vacuum. Each cylinder is anatomically flared at the lip for comfort. A complete system runs $95-$130. The CTC StudMaker is more primitive in design, using a rubber gasket and coming in only three sizes, but is cheaper at $69. It is also acceptable for the course. Electric pumps made by the above manufacturers are fine also, but should only be used by men who have had previous pumping experience. They are also more expensive, at $200-$500. For a complete tutorial on vacuum pumping, get a copy of Gary Griffin's *The Vacuum Pumper's Handbook*.

The photo on the following page shows precisely how vacuum pumping can increase the size of the penis. Take a look at the base of the penis (where it joins the body). Notice how the first couple of inches are slightly darker. This is where he

Condoms for the "big" man

❏   In his linguistic research, Gary Griffin has uncovered a possible link between the length of the tongue and the length of the penis. By 1995, enough evidence will be compiled to either support or refute this theory.

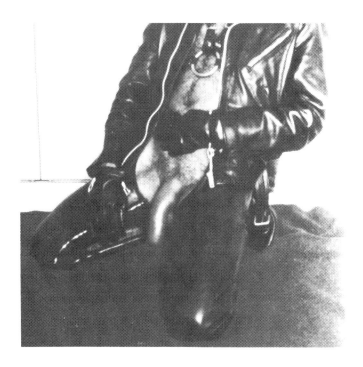

This man has gained 2" (5 cm) in length through several years of pumping.

How to 'add' an inch in 30 seconds

Here's a nifty trick for creating the illusion of a longer flaccid penis. A man's penis often appears smaller than it actually is, simply because the first inch or so of the shaft is hidden by a thick tuft of pubic hair. Following the outline of the sides of the penis, clear away this pubic hair by shaving straight up the shaft about an inch onto the pubis (shave only directly above the shaft). This will make the penis appear longer. Don't shave too high, though, or it will appear unnatural. By merely keeping the entire shaft clear of pubic hair, you will create the illusion of a longer penis.

❑   Many Italians claim that basil leaves can be used to increase penis size

has shaved back the pubic hair. Normally, pubic hair does not grow down this far on the shaft. What has happened is that the daily pumping has slowly stretched the suspensory ligament. Part of the pubic skin has actually been pulled out, adding to the penile "sock." This man has gained 2" (5 cm) over several years of vacuum pumping.

Conclusion: This is one of the few penis enlargement protocols that has been conducted in a scientific setting. If executed properly, most men achieve verifiable increases in size. Whereas the instructions recommend a 100 day program, Dr. Dick Richards states that actual results may require a much longer period of time. He recently wrote to me concerning the original trial conducted in the 1970s:

> Yes, I was very closely involved in the trials of the Chartham method. If my memory serves correctly...and it is too long ago to prove all that reliable, there were in fact three trials done. I personally did one of them. I'd have to guess it was about twenty years ago. I certainly did see the enlargements myself (tho' not ON myself as I was not a participant). The routine was that the patients were measured by me at something like two-weekly intervals. The results were published at the time but I doubt if anyone has copies. It is just remotely possible that there would be a copy somewhere in my archives, tho' even that seems unlikely.

> I recall that there were several other interesting factors that arose...and which were later confirmed when we repeated similar but rather more rigorous trials of the Penatone method in the early 80s. For example, at the start we interviewed most participants AND their wives/ girlfriends. For the most part they expressed unconcern and lack of enthusiasm about penis size. However, re-interviewed later when the trials were over there was a dramatic increase in those who found penis size interesting and valuable and who declared they were pleased with the increase and the unexpected effects this produced in themselves. At the time I had my doubts about penis size relevance. This, more than anything else, dispelled that misconception.

> I concur that the time period needed is certainly in excess of 100 days. That, I regard as the absolute minimum. Several months is better. This still applies in the case of Penatone (Penatone is the name of the penis enlargement course offered through the distributor, Dipix Distributions).

❑   How times have changed! Twenty five years ago, photographs of the nude male were considered obscene. Now, erotic magazines focusing on the nude male are freely sold over the counter in most mainstream bookstore chains.

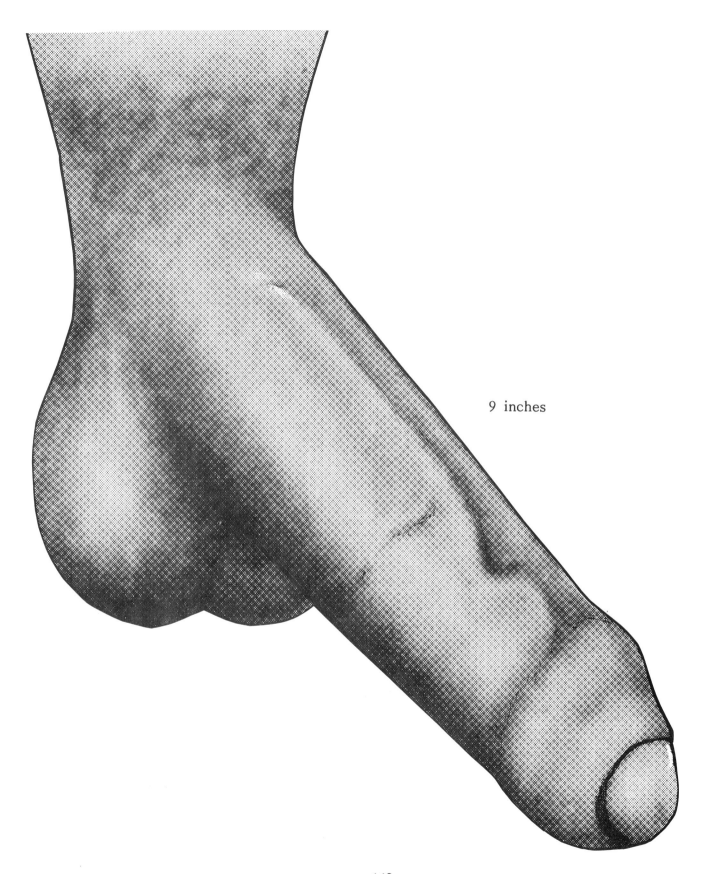

9 inches

142

For those of you who are interested in pursuing this course yourself, send $125 (if prices haven't increased) to: Dipix Distributions Ltd., 1 The Butchery, Sandwich, Kent CT13 9DL, England. Tell them you read about Penatone in this book. Give the course at least 6 months to see permanent results.

5 inches

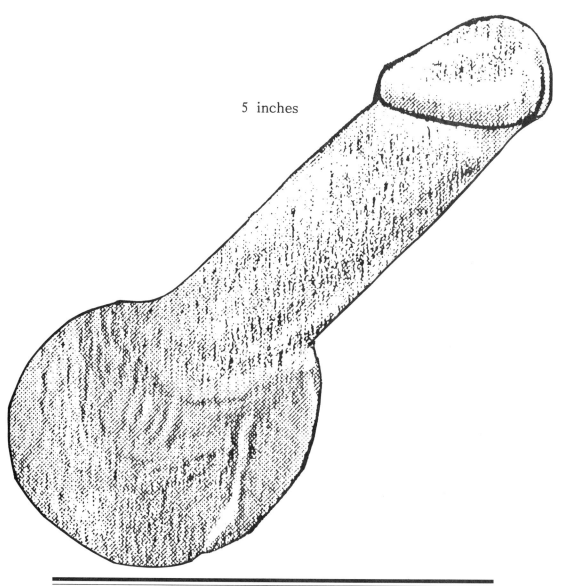

❏ It is estimated that 5-13% of doctors and mental health professionals have engaged in sexual contact with their patients.

Mental/Visual Imagery Enlargement Methods

These methods involve the use of hypnotism, auto-suggestion, and the power of the mind to increase the size of the organ. Before you shake your head in disbelief, know that mental power is showing great promise in the treatment of disease, depression, and a number of physical conditions. In his groundbreaking book, *Head First,* the late Norman Cousins presents case studies which clearly demonstrate the effectiveness of visualization and auto-suggestion in bringing about spontaneous remissions in a number of terminal diseases.

Due largely to Norman Cousins' efforts, a new branch of study, psychoneuroimmunology, has been introduced at UCLA's medical school to explore the connection between the mind and the physical body. The initial results are extremely encouraging, and in many medical circles, it is believed that future treatments of disease will incorporate a combination of drug therapy and auto suggestion.

Before his death in 1991, Mr. Cousins spent a great deal of time in individual consultation with severely ill patients who were not responding to last-ditch medical efforts. These patients had lost hope and feared that death was inevitable. Cousins' first task was to demonstrate that these people could take control of their illness. Using a simple "hand warming" technique described in *Head First* he showed how they could actually raise the temperature of their hands by five degrees of more. Energized by the new-found belief that they could activate such changes in their bodies by themselves, they practiced a series of auto-suggestive healing visualizations as directed by Mr. Cousins. In many cases, remarkable spontaneous remissions occurred, which could not be explained by any other means.

Best-selling author and Ayurvedic physician Deepak Chopra, M.D. has resurrected an ancient Indian medical practice which uses the mind to reverse any disease process and restore the body to a state of bliss and perfect health. Many of his precepts are based on the power of

---

❑ Men who want to display their anatomical bulge know that white, grey, and tan trousers are more revealing than darker colors.

transcendental meditation, which can allow an individual to literally take control of his mind, body, and spirit. This is how Indian swamis are able to comfortably rest on a bed of nails and perform other feats that boggle the mind. This same mental control can be used to augment body parts.

Auto suggestion and penis enlargement

What role does auto-suggestion play in penis enlargement? In 1974, it was clearly demonstrated that such methods could be successfully used to increase the size of the breast in women. In this pioneering study, 19 volunteer female university students were selected and divided into two groups--a study group and a control group. At the beginning of the study, breast measurements (inspired and expired) were taken followed by comparitive measurements at six and twelve weeks.

For the first six weeks, the subjects had a practice session in the clinic once a week. Using cassette tapes, the women were instructed to visualize a warm, wet towel over their breasts with an imaginary heat lamp providing additional warmth and stimulation. Once they were able to create the feeling of warmth in the breast tissues, they were asked to concentrate on the heart beat, allowing the pulse to bring additional blood and cell-building materials into the breast. They were asked to practice this technique at home on a daily basis. To enhance the effect of the visualization exercises, relaxation techniques and a self-induced hypnotic trance were also implemented.

The result? At the end of 12 weeks, 28% had reached their desired breast size and wished no further enlargement. Also, 85% of the participants perceived a significant enlargement in their breasts, while 46% found it necessary to purchase larger brassieres. After only twelve weeks, the average increase in bust size was 1.37" (for complete details, see *The Journal of Sex Research* vol 10, #4, pgs. 316-326, and *The American Journal of Clinical Hypnosis* vol 19, #4, pgs. 195-200). Dr. Richard Willard, M.D., of the "Institute of Behavioral and Mind Sciences" comments:

> This preliminary report shows that through hypnosis and visual imagery, the size of an organ can be affected and, specifically in this experiment, can be enlarged.

❑ Over the past decade, the treatment of impotence has truly revolutionized. Now, virtually 100% of impotent men can be successfully treated. Among the most popular treatments are penile injections--which result in erections lasting 30 minutes to 4 hours.

In support of this experiment, Florida hypnotherapist Michael Stivers developed a protocol using auto-suggestion for increasing the size of the bust. In 1992, he hit the talkshow circuit with several of his female clients--all of whom asserted that they had developed larger busts through his program. On the August 6, 1992 program of "The Maury Povich Show," Stivers outlined his program and demonstrated how his clients had gained an average of 2-4" (4-8 cm) in bust size. He asserted that this same protocol could be applied to any part of the body. Following the show, I contacted Mr. Stivers and asked him if he ever considered developing a parallel program for men. Coincidentally, he had just enrolled three men in an experimental penis enlargement program using hypnosis. At the time of our conversation, one of the three (a doctor) had exhibited a verifiable increase in penis size.

In August, 1993, I contacted talented LA hypynotherapist Jim Pifer, who studied with the legendary stage hypnotist, Pat Collins. I presented the idea of developing a program for genital enlargement through auto-suggestion and hypnosis. He was very amenable and spent the next several weeks developing a protocol, inviting me and another man to participate as trial subjects. After explaining his program, he invited us into his living room where we both relaxed in comfortable, cushy recliners. As soft, ethereal music played in the background, he brought us to a deep level of relaxation and suggestibility. Then he invited us to mentally enter a department store, walk up to the catalog counter and flip through the pages of the catalog. This was no consumer-goods catalog, but rather a cock compendium with each page showcasing a different penis. Perusing the catalog, we were instructed to find the particular penis that appealed to us the most. Once we located the ideal organ, we were to assign it a three-digit catalog number. Then, he regressed us to the point of conception when the sperm cell penetrated the ovum. He had us visually enter the egg and locate the particular strand of DNA where penis size is determined. With mental scissors, we snipped out our current penis genes and replaced them with the "new, improved" strand with the three digit catalog number and the picture of our ideal penis.

Once accomplished, we visualized our fetus developing with a prominent penis. As we entered the world, we watched the doctor and nurses comment on the unusually-large sized penis. Puberty and adolescence brought about an incredibly-rapid rate of genital development, resulting in a penis much larger than that of the average adult male. We could visualize

❏   In New Guinea, several tribes hold contests to determine which male can ejaculate the farthest.

our penises being the object of admiration and adulation of our peers in the locker room. At age 18, we were to picture ourselves with our catalog cocks hanging halfway down our legs--pendulously long, beercan-thick, and veiny.

Before being brought out of the hypnotic state, we were given special subliminal messages to increase the effectiveness of the program. Using clues from the new field of neurolinguistic programming, he incorporated specific verbal cues to use as subliminal anchors. Each time we would hear a certain word or make a certain gesture, it would reinforce the message of larger penis size. After four sessions, we were taught how to hypnotize ourselves and were instructed to perform the auto-suggestion sequence 5-10 minutes each day. To further cement the visual impact, we were instructed to take a full body picture of ourselves (nude) and paste the image (from a photograph) of our ideal penis between our legs. This would allow us to see how we would actually look with our desired organs. Each time we looked in the mirror, we were to visualize ourselves with this new penis.

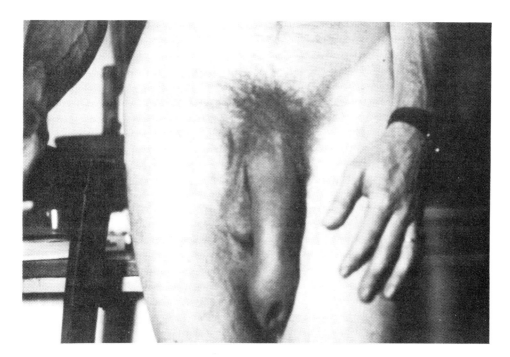

An astounding 10" (25 cm) Swedish penis

❑ Phalloplasty augmentation (surgical girth enhancement of the penis) runs $2,500-$4,000.

147

RACA

No discussion on auto suggestion and genital enlargement would be complete without mention of Ray Carlton. A veteran penis enlarger, Ray started out with an average 6" (15 cm) organ at age 20. After 10 years of pumping, he increased his length to 8" (20 cm), but still wasn't satisfied. Ray claims that he received a miraculous healing from a physical ailment and through meditation and study, developed an effective program for enlarging the organ. Ray now measures an astounding 10 1/4" (26 cm) and his photos prove that he is indeed a "horseman." His eventual goal is 15" (38 cm) long by 8" (20 cm) around. Ray's program consists of meditation, visual imagery, and a few other surprises. For complete instructions, send $15 to: RACA, Box 819, Perry, FL, 32347-0819.

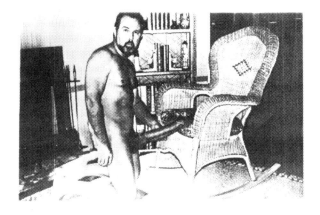

Ray Carlton's equine phallus

Conclusion: The possibility of penis enlargement through guided visual imagery, hypnotism, and autosuggestion is truly exciting. The research is still too new to draw conclusions, but this is an area we will be watching closely. Possibly the best results will be achieved when auto suggestion is used in conjunction with vacuum pumping and daily penis milking. Stay tuned to *Penis Power Quarterly* for the latest updates in this area.

❑   Surgical lengthening (or advancement) of the penis averages $3,500.

GENETIC MANIPULATION

Penis size, like eye color, stature, build, and skin tone, is inherited. If your father or grandfather was hung, chances are that you are also well-endowed. The key to inherited penis size is locked up in the mysteries of DNA--that double helix of genetically-encoded information. Long stretches of DNA are identical in all people. After all, we all have ears, feet, kidneys, and so on. But specific strands of DNA vary dramatically from one individual to another. In these strands, short sequences of "junk DNA" appear. These areas, whose functions are still not clearly understood, repeat themselves over and over like a broken record. In these highly variable regions, we are able to identify the characteristics that distinguish one person from all others on the planet--hair and eye color, nose shape, blood type, height, and yes, penis size. Each individual (save for identical twins) has a unique "junk DNA" pattern. Forensic scientists now use these DNA prints (which can be isolated from a single drop of saliva, semen, or blood) as powerful tools to connect a suspected criminal to a particular crime.

Researchers have recently embarked upon one of the most ambitious scientific projects ever undertaken by man. Through international cooperation and the use of high-speed computers, scientists intend to create a comprehensive "gene map" or "encyclopedia" of the hundreds of thousands of genes that comprise DNA. When completed sometime in the next century, scientists will be able to identify the specific genes that contribute to hereditary diseases. In addition, we will know precisely which genes make our eyes blue, our hair curly, or cause freckles. And yes, the DNA sequence that determines penis size will also be identified, and genetic engineers may be able to custom manufacture a penis to your precise order. I'm sure the donkey size will be the most popular!

Two types of genetic manipulation are envisioned--**somatic gene therapy** and **germ line therapy**. In the former, genes are tweaked to bring about changes in your body without affecting the genes of your offspring. WIth germ line therapy, any genetic manipulation will not only permanently alter your personal genetic makeup, but that of your progeny as well. It is thought that any cosmetic manipulation will involve somatic gene therapy.

❑ Most male models bring themselves to a state of moderate sexual excitement before being photographed so that the penis hangs at its maximum flaccid dimensions--making it appear larger than it normally would.

149

Hormonal administration

Urologists have learned that when testosterone is applied to the organs of young boys suffering from micropenia, phallic growth can be stimulated. An abstract that appeared in the March 1980 edition of the *American Journal of the Disabled Child*, Ehud Ben-Galim, M.D., Richard E. Hillman, M.D., and Virginia V. Weldon, M.D., applied a topical solution of 5% testosterone cream for 21 days to the penises of five boys with normal XY karyotype suffering from microphallus (extremely small penises) and hypopituitarism. The levels of testosterone rose from that of an infant to that of a normal adult male on the last day of treatment. In addition, all five boys were receiving human growth hormone at the time of therapy. Each of the five demonstrated significant phallic growth approaching normal levels at the cessation of therapy.

More recently, another trial has been conducted, applying topical dihydrotestosterone to the penises of 22 boys ranging in age from 3 to 15. All of these males were suffering from micropenia. The protocol lasted a total of 8 weeks during which time those under age 10 received a daily dosage of 12.5 mg. while those over 10 received 25 mg. At the end of the trial (see *Journal of Urology* August 1993), 12 (55%) reported "good" results while the remaining 10 (45%) reported "fair" results. All had experienced increases the size of their penis, with a mean increase of 153%. Interestingly, the older boys (those entering puberty) achieved better results than the younger boys. Researchers theorize that during puberty, the effects of the chemical 5-alpha reductase (which may stunt phallic growth) is decreased, and this may accentuate the activity of the dihydrotestosterone.

Prenatally, hormonal administration can greatly affect the phallic development of the fetus. In the first 12-14 weeks of the fetus' development, the quantity of testosterone we produce is predicated upon our mother's hormones. After this time, our own production kicks in. If insufficient hormone is produced during the first 12-14 weeks, the development of the phallus may be stunted, resulting in microphallus. Women who take sex hormones to discourage miscarriage run the risk of retarding the growth of their son's penis. At 10 weeks, the fetus' penis grows approximately .03" per week, growing from 0.1" to an average streched length of 1 1/2" (4 cm.) at birth.

❏   One of the most unusual exhibitions in the U.S. is the Lifestyles Convention, in which exhibits of anything sexual, from erotic art to dildos to pornographic videos are prominently displayed. Highlights of this 3-day affair include the group massage session and the clothing optional ball.

I have heard of cases where the mother took specific hormones (although I can't get verification on the specific drug) during the first trimester of pregnancy. The sons of these women developed abnormally large penises which couldn't be contributed to genetics or heredity. Obviously, the right hormone (and proper dosage) can encourage phallic growth far beyond the normal, while the wrong hormone can result in microphallus.

A recent article in *Newsweek* confirmed the fact that penises may be getting smaller, thanks to the lingering effects of DDT on the environment. It appears that when DDT breaks down, it decomposes into a number of estrogen-related chemicals. Since DDT has a very long half-life and remains in the ground for years, it is inevitable that it enters the food supply. Already, zoologists have noted that alligators in the Everglades now sport micropenises that measure barely 1/4 the size of their fathers. This is directly attributable to high levels of DDT in the Everglades. Likewise, many cases of micropenis in humans may be attributable to incidental ingestion of DDT by gestating mothers. Indeed, unless we change our polluting habits and discover ways of removing DDT from contaminated soils, we can expect more and more boys to be born with extremely small organs.

In addition, we are discovering that women who took the anti-miscarriage drug, DES, in the 1940s and '50s, may have unwittingly passed on problems to their sons. Testicular cancer has increased 200% and prostate cancer 300% in the past 40 years, according to the television newsmagazine, *20/20*. Stunted penis growth may also be attributable to DES.

Conclusion: Testosterone and dihydrotestosterone therapy certainly works well on young boys, especially those suffering from micropenia. However, after adolescence, the administration of testosterone or dihydrotestosterone to males with normal levels of the hormone can have deleterious consequences and certainly will NOT increase the size of the penis. To date, no one has conducted studies on boys wil average-sized penises. It is entirely possible that the administration of dihydrotestosterone to pubescent boys with normal phallic development could turn their penises into equine-sized weapons. No one knows for sure, since most doctors would consider such an experiment medically irresponsible.

Along this same line, I received a letter from a reader in South Carolina who related a fascinating story. The town doctor, who provided physical examinations to the high school athletes, allegedly injected a group

---

❑ From the "truly bizarre" file...did you know that when the husband of a Tasmanian woman dies, the law requires that she wear her dead husband's penis around her neck. The aboriginal women in Gippsland, Australia, are required to do the same.

of boys with a secret hormonal preparation. Within months, each boy had developed a penis of stupendous dimensions. Unfortunately, attempts to contact this doctor and learn more of his specific protocol have been futile. He is retired, in his 80s, and will not discuss his injections for fear of legal retribution. One thing is for certain, however. None of these boys (now horse-hung men) have any plans to sue the doctor!

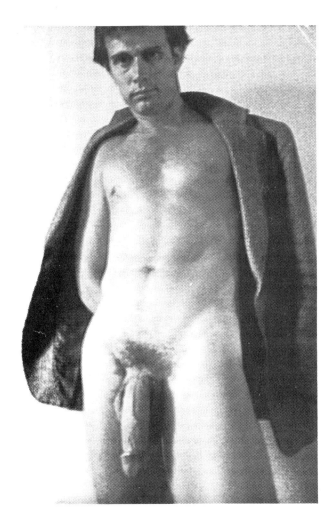

The size penis most men dream of

❏ Among the strangest organs is that of the pig, whose penis is corkscrew-shaped.

SURGICAL METHODS

The penis finally emerged from the closet big time when, in 1991, news was leaked about a Florida plastic surgeon who had developed a procedure for increasing the girth of the penis through fat injections. This event signalled a watershed in the era of male sexuality. Apart from impotence, seldom, if ever, was the penis considered a socially-acceptable topic of discussion. But with the emergence of surgical enlargement, thousands of men around the world began requesting information on how they could avail themselves of this new procedure. Within months, interest was so great that talkshows were clamoring for doctors and patients who could offer their personal insights on surgical enlargement. Now, barely a couple of years after the first patient underwent surgical enlargement, more than a dozen surgeons around the world are offering the procedure.

Although surgical enlargement first came to popular attention in 1991, it is actually much older. In the 1970s, an American surgeon (who allegedly lost his license to practice in the U.S.) opened a clinic in Tijuana, Mexico offering a cornucopia of genital enhancement operations including such iconoclastic and experimental procedures as glans enlargement, root advancement, and silicone injections. The latter was an especially heinous undertaking. Although the increase was immediate and impressive, the material had the propensity of gravitating toward the middle of the penis, over time resulting in an unappealing donut effect. We now know the dangers associated with implanted liquid silicone. Many men who had the injections 10-20 years ago are now beginning to suffer the deleterious consequences. Some have even had the silicone surgically-removed. Another drawback was that the procedure added only girth--it did nothing to lengthen the penis or increase the size of the glans. This could make the penis look completely out of proportion. Fortunately, this surgeon has now gone into retirement.

Earlier, in the 1960s, a Dr. Bihari in Egypt developed a procedure for increasing the length of the penis. Hundreds of desperate and adventurous men spent considerable sums of money to fly to Cairo and have this unorthodox procedure performed. The results were mixed. Some men

---

❑ Fertility specialists recommend that their male patients switch from briefs to boxers to increase the production of sperm.

153

alleged that their penises increased in length up to 2" while others perceived no net gain. However, the initial enthusiasm for this procedure soon trickled to a whisper, being tempered by the marginal results and the high cost. By the 1970s, men in increasing numbers began turning to safer, less-invasive options such as vacuum pumping, which has now become a popular subrosa sexual sport practiced by thousands of devotees around the world.

Penis girth enhancement

Ricardo Samitier, M.D., finally legitimized penis enlargement in 1991. Known as the plastic surgeon who popularized the fuller lip look through fat injections (a la Julia Roberts), he began toying with the possibility of increasing the girth of the penis via the same method. Practicing on cadavers, he developed a method that looked promising, but needed live subjects to test the viability of lipotransfer. Appearing on a Spanish language radio station in Miami he appealed for volunteers to try his largely untested procedure. He returned to his office hoping for a message or two. To his utter amazement, within four hours he had received over 100 calls from men desperately seeking larger penises.

After narrowing down the list of volunteers to a dozen candidates, he brought them in one by one and performed the procedure. The results were very encouraging and virtually all of the men were ecstatic with their newly-enlarged penises. One man wrote back and said that for the first time in his married life, his wife screamed in ecstacy during intercourse.

The lipotransfer (taking fat from one part of the body and implanting it elsewhere on the body) procedure is quite simple. A simple liposuction is performed on the abdomen (occasionally on the pubis, medial thigh, or buttocks) in which a cup (approximately) of fat is removed. This fat is washed and specially prepared before being reinjected under the skin of the penis. The results are immediate and impressive. Gains of up to 1" (2.5 cm) or more are not uncommon.

There are drawbacks though. The procedure is expensive--costing $2000-$4,000, and invariably a certain amount of reaborption (usually 30-70% or more) will occur over time. The specific fat preparation techniques largely determine the viability of the fat cells and how much will

❏   Queen Johanna I of Naples believed in the maxim "Nasatorum peculio" (Big nose, big hose) when she married Prince Andrew of Hungary in 1343. Her husband's organ turned out to be much less than advertised. She lamended "Oh nose, how horribly you have deceived me."

eventually be reabsorbed. Also, some instances of fat cysts and fibro-fatty nodules (harmless and easily removed) are reported. Note that virtually all medical organizations have labeled this procedure as experimental. Some of the surgeons who initially performed penile lipotransfer (also known as phalloplasty augmentation) have since abandoned it, while others have added it to their surgical repertoire. Over the past couple of years, my enthusiasm for this lipotransfer technique has waned. I've seen too many complications to continue to recommend it with any degree of enthusiasm. Several doctors assert that their particular techniques have avoided the problems with reabsorption and nodules, but I haven't seen a great deal of difference in results from one doctor to another.

However, there is a bright spot on the horizon of penile girth enhancement. Several new techniques have recently been developed which represent major improvements over lipotransfer--dermal fat grafts, live tissue transfer, and inflatable prostheses

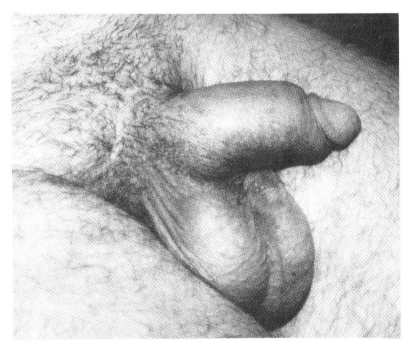

Notice the impressive girth of this penis which has been surgically enlarged.

❏   A major adult magazine "Down Under" recently held a contest to determine the largest penis in Australia. The winner allegedly sported a member
that measured 11 1/2" in length.

An uncircumcised male--a relative rarity in the U.S. Only 10-15% of American adults remain "intact"

Dermal fat graft

In early 1994, two doctors independently developed a method that would largely obviate the problems of lipotransfer while producing cosmetically-appealing results. This newer method is known as the "dermal fat graft." This technique is more complicated and intricate than the simpler lipotransfer, therefore, more time and skill is involved. However, the ultimate results appear to be more permanent and cosmetically pleasing.

Here's how it's done. While under anesthesia, the patient is placed on his stomach. The entire buttocks and thigh areas are scrubbed with an antibacterial preparation. The surgeon then uses a surgical pen to carefully mark the places from which the donor fat will be extracted--usually the gluteal fold (this is the crease where you thigh meets the buttocks). The surgeon will make a fairly large incision (8" to 10") on each gluteal fold and will then carefully extract a strip of fat, removing the epidermis (outer layer of skin). The incisions are then sewn up.

The patient is then flipped over and the doctor then makes an incision on each side of the penile shaft in preparation for the insertion of the fat strips. The doctor cuts down to the layer of tissue known as *Buck's fascia*. The outer layers of the penile skin are then separated from the underlying tissues and the fat graft is carefully positioned and tucked into the penis. The incisions are then sewed together with the fat grafts in place.

This procedure can take 2-3 hours--and when penile lengthening is added (resection of the suspensory ligament) the operation can take 3-4 hours or more. The advantages of the dermal fat graft over the old lipotransfer method are many. First, the results appear to be more permanent. Due to the fact that the vascularity (blood vessels) remains intact, there is a much higher degree of fat cell survivability (although graft rejection does seem to occur in 4-5% of cases). Second, since each graft consists of a large strip of intact fat, the penis can be made much thicker than with the lipotransfer method. Also, one of the benefits of this technique is that the incision is made in a natural crease, so that any scarring will be very inconspicuous. Also, the sutures will naturally tighten up the buttocks--meaning that you get a free gluteoplasty or "butt lift."

At the time of this writing, approximately 6 surgeons have abandoned the lipotransfer method in favor of the dermal fat graft procedure. As it is still fairly new, it is too early to draw conclusions regarding the long-term viability, but so far, it looks to be an improvement over lipotransfer.

___

❑   Japan uses more condoms per capita than any other nation in the world.

Dermal fat graft (before)

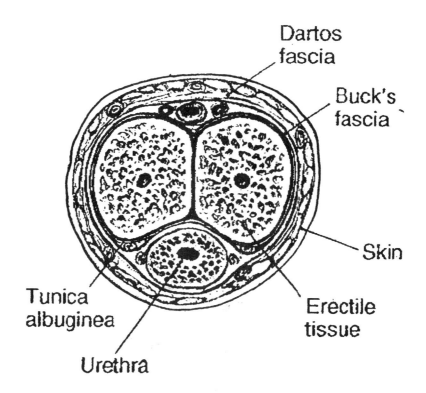

Dartos fascia

Buck's fascia

Skin

Erectile tissue

Tunica albuginea

Urethra

❑   The average increase in circumference from the dermal fat graft procedure is 2"

.

.

.

Dermal fat graft (after)

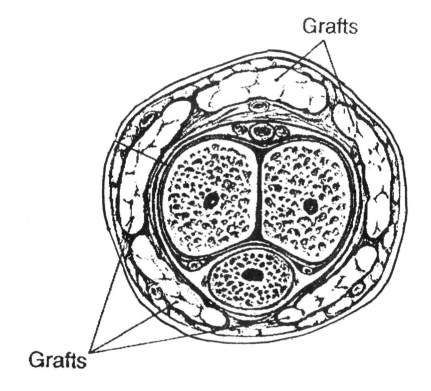

Notice how the donor fat strips are implanted between the skin and Buck's fascia. The results are immediate and impressive.

(Illustrations courtesy of urologist Gary Alter, MD)

❏ Fully 3-4" of the penis are contained INSIDE the body. This is the "anchor" of the penis, known medically as the crura.

Glans enlargement

One of the most frequent questions I receive from readers is whether or not the glans can be enlarged. Unfortunately, the answer is no. The glans (head of the penis) is composed of an entirely different tissue than the rest of the penis. Whereas the shaft of the penis is composed of twin cylinders of hollow, inflatable tissues (corpora cavernosa). The glans, on the other hand is more of a solid, spongy mass (corpora spongiosum). Fat can be implanted along the shaft to increase the girth, but not in the glans.

However, urological surgeon, Gary Rheinschild, MD of Anaheim, CA, has developed a specialized technique in which small strips of fat harvested from the dermal fat graft procedure can be tucked under the glans to effectively increase the perceived size of the glans. The mushroom-shaped glans will actually flare out slightly.

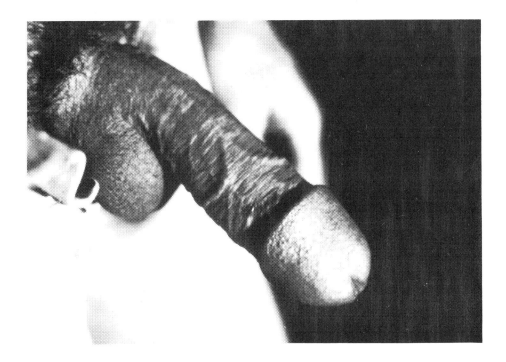

A penis with a large glans--which most men and women find aesthetically pleasing and providing more vaginal stimulation during intercourse.

❏　　A "micropenis" is one that measures less than 4" in the erect state. Approximately 5% of the adult male population suffers from this condition.

160

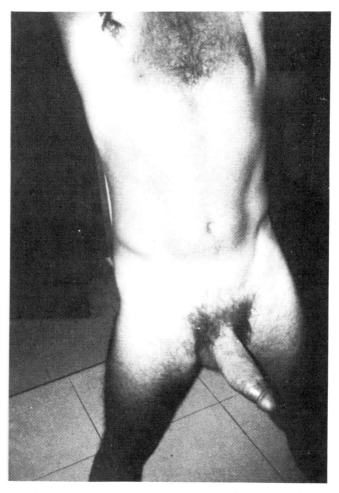

This large penis has a proportionately-small glans. Unfortunately, the glans doesn't respond favorably to current enlargement technology.

Penises come in all sizes and shapes, and the glans is no exception. Some men proudly sport large, well-formed glanses while others may be small and recessive. This can be a problem to those men who have had their penile shafts augmented by one of the fat transfer procedures. The newly-enlarged shaft can actually make the glans appear smaller. This new glans enhancement procedure can make the glans appear more in proportion with the rest of the penis.

❑   Some men infuse their scrota with saline IV infusions for temporary enlargement. This can increase the size of the scrotum from the size of a grapefruit to that of a canteloupe. The saline gradually reabsorbs into the body within 48 hours, however.

Dr. Rheinschild remarks that glans enhancement is not possible for every man. In most males, the glans can be surgically lifted from the underlying tissue to permit the insertion of a small strip of fat. However, the anatomy of some men does not permit this. Unfortunately, there is no way to determine who is a good candidate for glans enhancement until surgery is underway. If you are blessed with an impressive, helmet-shaped glans in the first place, you won't need to consider the enhancement.

The future of surgical glans enhancement is very much in doubt. The glans is a difficult tissue to work with and its true benefit is in question. Perhaps improvements in technique will render this a more viable procedure in the future, but for now it should be considered nothing more than experimental.

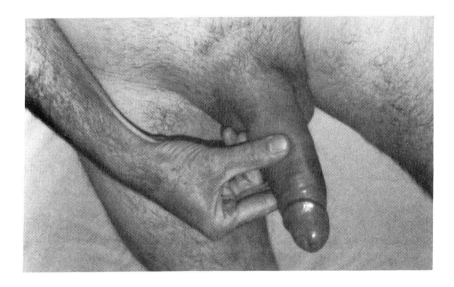

This penis was surgically enlarged and lengthened by Harold Reed, MD. Notice the small incision in the pubic area.

❑   Renard Industries of Tulsa, OK (800) 225-1670 has developed a brief with a detachable cloth dildo that provides the impression of a large penis.

Live Tissue Transfer

Doctors are continually looking for improvements in surgical penile girth enhancement, and live tissue transfer is the latest development. Developed by noted sex-change surgeon Donald Laub, MD, the procedure involves making an incision in the pubic area (the same incision is used in the penile lengthening process) and cutting a rectangle of fat. When this portion of fat is loosened from the overlying dermis (skin) it is pulled out of the incision and "flipped over" where it is then tucked directly into the penis. Remember that this rectangle of fat is not totally severed from the body--only three sides. The side closest to the penis remains intact in order to maintain the vascularity (blood flow) of the fat tissue.

As with the dermal fat graft, live tissue transfer is still in its infancy and long term results are not yet available. Dr. Gary Rheinschild, who has been performing live tissue transfer for several months, says that there is no way to determine which procedure (dermal fat graft vs. live tissue transfer) is better suited for the individual patient until he has the chance to look inside the incision. Apparently, the quality of the pubic fat, the weight of the patient, and several other factors determines the physician's choice.

The Elist Inflatable Prosthesis

Just days before this book went to press, I received a call from Dr. James Elist, a Beverly Hills urologist. He informed me that he had finally received a patent on an intriguing new device for permanently enlarging the penis.

A year earlier, I was the guest of Dr. Elist at a tony Rodeo bistro. Over a steaming plate of pasta primavera, Dr. Elist animatedly described his concept--at that time still in the theoretical stages. He explained that his prosthesis consists of an inert, inflatable material that is surgically implanted under the skin of the penis. It is then "inflated" with saline to the precise size desired by the patient. Its mesh network design allows for the natural flow of blood in a around the device. It is still too early to draw conclusions as to the long-term viability of this device, but we will be following the developments closely in *Penis Power Quarterly.*

❑   The angle of the erection tends to decrease slightly with age.

Testicular enlargement

Many men feel that their testicles are not as large as they'd like. Competitive body builders, swimmers, and models are particularly concerned with this issue as many feel that they don't show enough "masculine bulge" in tight-fitting briefs and swimwear. Previous attempts to enlarge the scrotum through fat injections and saline have been less than impressive as both only provide temporary enlargement. And even surgically-implanted fat seems to reabsorb within a period of months.

A more permanent solution is now at hand. Dr. James Elist has developed a prosthesis that is surgically implanted in the tunica vaginalis (the membrane surrounding the testicle) to permanently increase the size of the testes. The implants come in three sizes--medium, large, and extra large. The cost for the procedure as of this writing is $2,500.

An already impressive penis which has been surgically-enlarged.

❑ A note to bodybuilders--long term steroid usage can drastically reduce the size of the testicles!

164

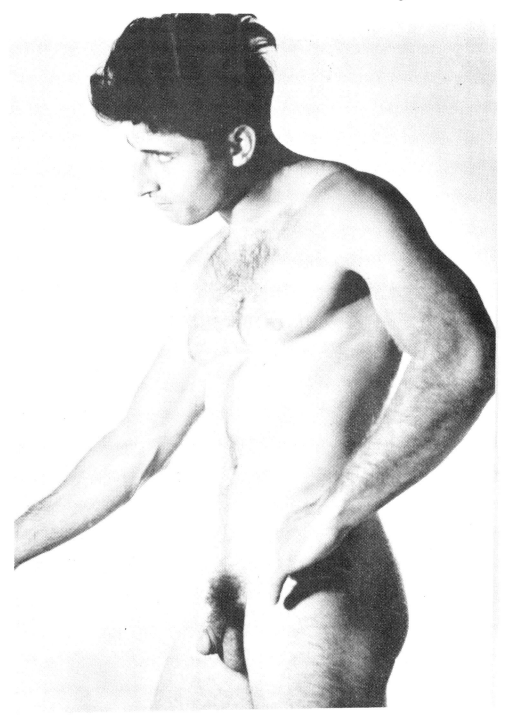

A small penis measuring 4-5" when erect.

Some doctors express concern about the implantation of a foreign substance in the scrotum. Rejection and implant failure are legitimate concerns, but remember that foreign substances are successfully implanted in the body all the time--pacemakers, heart valves, breast implants, etc. Long term studies will hopefully resolve the issues regarding the viability of testicular implants.

Several non-surgical methods of scrotal enlargement have been developed by men over the years. They vary in degrees of success and safety. For more information, refer to my book, *Testicles--The Ball Book.*

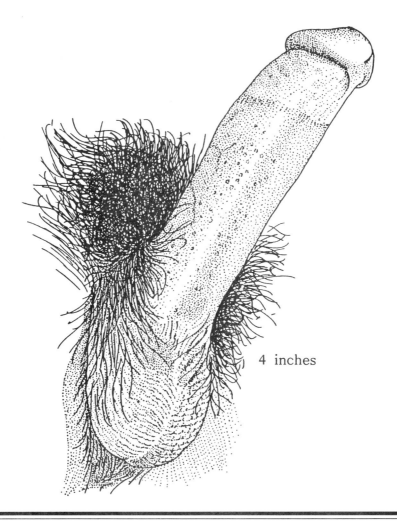

4 inches

❑   Two commonly-prescribed medications have been shown to dramatically improve premature ejaculation.

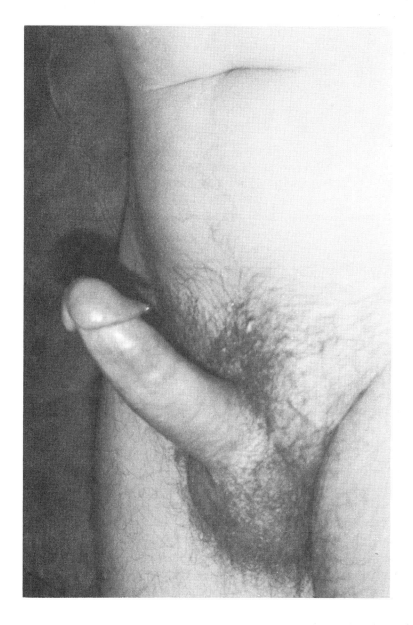

An average-sized penis that measures 5-7" when erect. 75% of all men fall within this erect size range.

Penile lengthening

In this procedure, no actual length is created, rather, the internal portion of the penis is "advanced" or "externalized," creating the impression of greater length. This is accomplished by resecting (cutting) a portion of the suspensory ligament which holds the penis upward during erection (see illustration). A simple lesson in penile anatomy will help you understand how

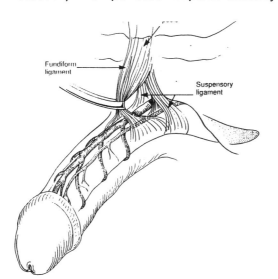

this procedure can add an inch or so to your penis. What you see when you view your own penis in the mirror is the **external portion**, which is just "the tip of the iceberg," so to speak. Actually, another 3-4" of the penis is located IN-SIDE the body. Known medically as the *crux* or *crura*, this is the root which anchors the penis to the body. This penile root actually arches upward inside the body, and by resecting the suspensory ligament, this upward is leveled out so that it takes a "straight shot" out of the body. A simple 2-3" transverse or curvilinear incision in the pubic area is all that is required. For overweight men, removal of some of the fat in the pubic area will also add to the perceived length increase of the penis.

There are several variations on surgical penile lengthening which involve different incisions--a curvilinear incision, a straight-across incision, a "Y"-shaped incision, and an "M"-shaped incision. Each doctor has his preferred method. Some doctors claim that the "Y" or "M"-shaped incisions provide better results, but my research fails to indicate a significant difference. What seems to matter more is the post-surgical wearing of a weighted device, such as the P.L.D.™ device. This modular weight helps the penis heal at its maximum length. If not worn, the scar tissue may retract the

❏ The human male has the largest penis (proportional to body) of all bipeds.

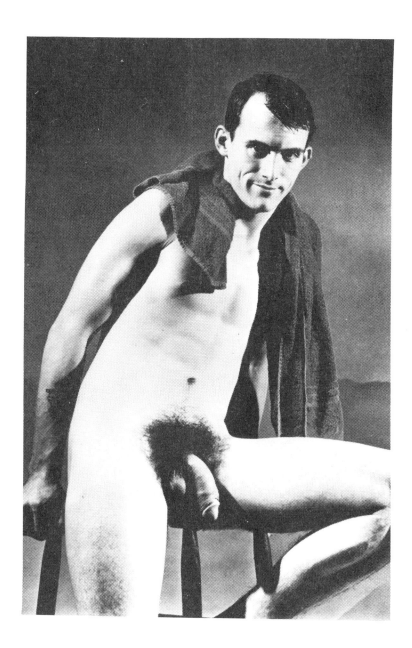

A large penis which measures over 7" when erect. Only 10% of all men are this size or larger.

penis back to its former position--thereby obviating the results of the surgery. A few doctors claim that their techniques are so good that the weight is not needed. I disagree. I believe that the weight provides greater assurance that the maximum amount of length will be gained.

What is absolutely paramount is to locate a board certified surgeon with extensive experience. Some doctors are highly skilled in this procedure while others are less experienced. One particular doctor advertises in newspapers and magazines throughout the U.S. claiming that the average man will "double in size," gaining between 2-3". This is sheer medical hyperbole and will never happen. This doctor, by the way, is facing a number of lawsuits. Stay away.

May I again stress that the most important decision you can make is to find the right doctor. As the executive director of the "American Association of Phalloplasty Surgeons" I have become acquainted with most of the doctors performing surgical enlargement and feel I am a fair judge of their skill level and attention to patient care. But my subjective evaluations are not enough. The best way to judge a doctor is to ask his patients how satisfied they are with their surgical results and level of care. I have asked my readers who have undergone phalloplasty augmentation to rank their surgeons in regards to results, service, staff, and aftercare. The results are printed in *Penis Power Quarterly.* Among the surgeons, there are 5-6 that do excellent work and take outstanding care of their patients. For a recommendation, drop me a line or refer to *PPQ.*

Be particularly wary of doctors who place slick ads in newspapers and men's magazines. These doctors often make outlandish promises that can't be fulfilled. In particular, stay away from those clinics that invite you in for a free consultation. Rarely will you meet the doctor. Instead, you will be pressured by a commissioned salesman whose sole duty is to get you to sign on the dotted line. Two surgeons that I recommend highly are Gary Rheinschild, M.D., 1211 W. La Palma Ave. Suite #303, Anaheim, CA 92801 (714) 956-9532 or (800) 427-3150 and Harold Reed, M.D., 1111 Kane Concourse, Bay Harbor Island, FL 33154 (305) 865-2000. For other recommendations, refer to *Penis Power Quarterly,* or call my 900 number for the complete lowdown on surgical enlargement (900) 933-7676. The cost is 95 cents per minute.

❏ A number of specialty "erotic" bakeries have sprung up in metropolitan areas of U.S. cities Their most-requested items are cakes in the shapes of the male and female genitalia.

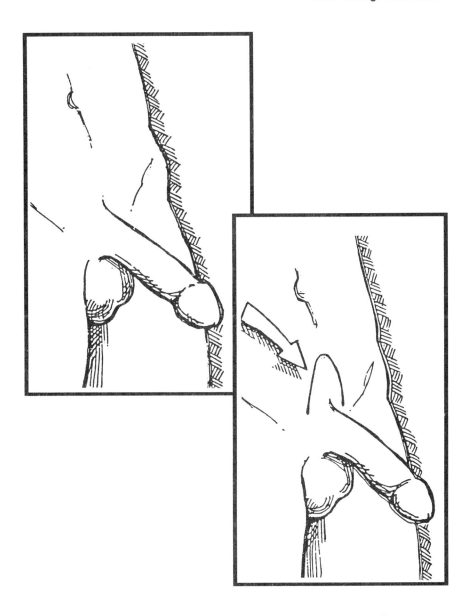

These illustrations demonstrate how the resection of the suspensory ligament creates the illusion of a longer penis. In the second illustration, an inverted "V"-shaped incision is made. (Illustrations courtesy of Hennie Roos, MD)

❑   The fly on mens' trousers is the last vestige of the codpiece--which went out of fashion some 400 years ago.

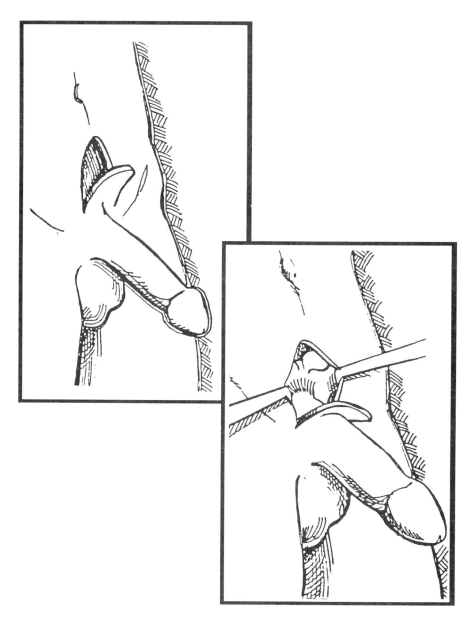

The incision is spread apart with retractors to expose the underlying suspensory ligament.

❑   When being fitted for a new pair of trousers, the tailor may ask if you "dress left" (wear your penis to the left) or "dress right" (wear your penis to the right". More than 75% of all men dress left.

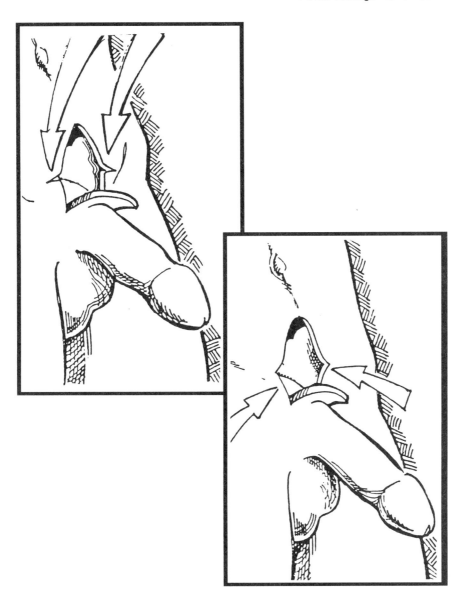

After the suspensory ligament is cut, the penis is pulled down and the two sides of
the incisions are drawn together

❑   The degree of sexual arousal often determines the trajectory and distance
     of ejaculation.

173

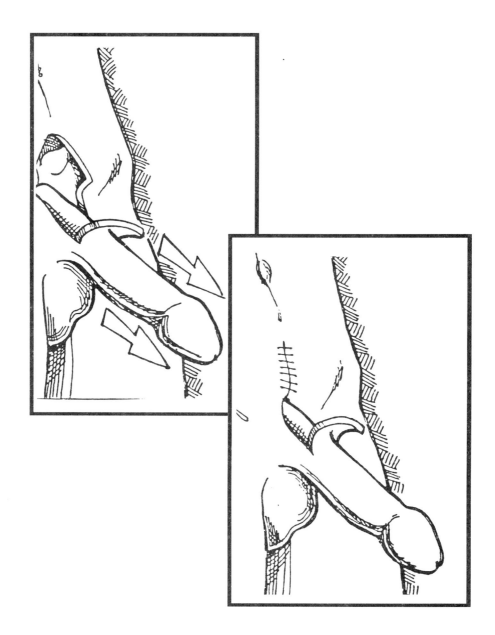

The incision is then sutured.

❏   After urination, half of all surveyed males shake the penis while half milk
      the shaft

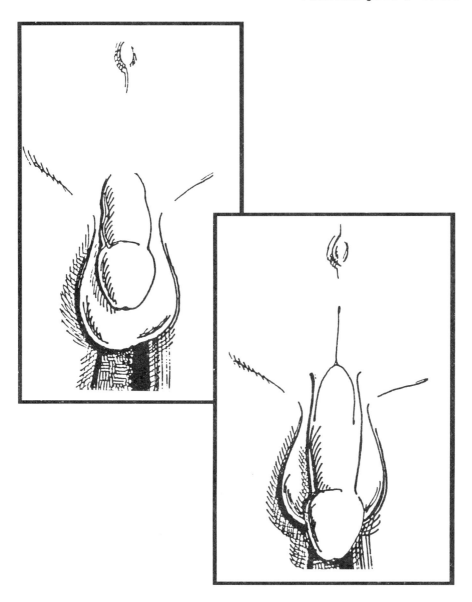

Before and after comparisons. Notice the position of the glans in relation to the scrotum. In the "before" illustration, the scrotum is longer than the glans. The reverse is apparent in the "after" illustration.

❑   Some Indian gurus have developed sexual stimulation to an art. It is reported that they are able to achieve erection and ejaculation solely through mental concentration. No hands are used.

175

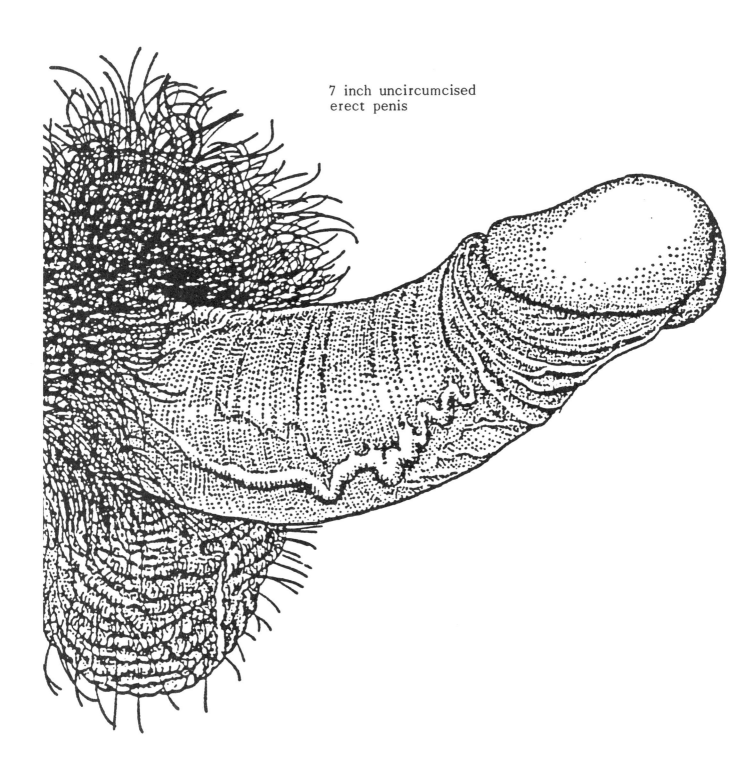

7 inch uncircumcised
erect penis

❏ If you are dissatisfied with your circumcision status, get "The Joy of Uncircumcision" by Jim Bigelow, Ph.D. (Hourglass Book Publishing, Aptos, CA.)

The above is merely a glimpse into the ever-changing world of surgical penile enlargement. A much more detailed look is provided in my book, *Straight talk about surgical penis enlargement.* Read this book if you considering the procedure. Also, stay tuned to *Penis Power Quarterly* for up-to-the-minute updates in this area.

Conclusion: Surgical penis enlargement is expensive--costing between $2,500-$4,000 for a single procedure to $4,000-$6,500 for both girth and length. While still considered experimental, both procedures deserve close watching as increasing numbers of men flock to qualified surgeons for larger cocks. With the old lipotransfer method, the main concerns are fat cysts and reabsorption. Complications with the newer dermal fat graft and live tissue transfer are less common, but remember that long term results are not yet available. What deserves close observation is the inflatable prosthesis which may eventually do away with fat transplants altogether. If done correctly, the results of penile girth enhancement can be stroking. Conversely, if done poorly or haphazadly, the results can be devastating.. Again, the keys are finding the right doctor and following his post-op instructions explicitly.

The lengthening procedure doesn't always provide the increases one hopes for. The increases are more apparent in the flaccid state than during erection. If locker room appearances are a concern to you, this procedure may be worth your while as you will definitely hang longer when soft. Many surgical enlargees, however, comment that they notice little or no change in the erect state. A few men have even complained that the resulting scar tissue retracted their penises--causing them to LOSE length! No one wants to pay thousands of dollars for a smaller penis, so again, make sure that you choose the right doctor.

A few studies are underway to ascertain the patient's satisfaction with surgical enlargement. A small study conducted at Northwestern University found that of 50 patients, not one was totally satisfied. However, 28 of these 50 men said that they would do it again. This mixed message tells us that surgical enlargement, while not living up to its inflated hype, does produce modest results which may be worth the money for some men.

The lengthening procedure can be performed separately or concur-rently with girth enhancement. For both procedures, gains of 1/4" - 2" (1.5 -

---

❏   The average male experiences 4-6 erections during sleep each night.

5 cm) can be expected although no guarantees can be made. The most dramatic gains are apparent in the flaccid state. Some men gain very little in erect length, but virtually all men achieve notiiceable gains in the flaccid state, which can improve one's confidence in locker room situations. One must be prepared for modest results. Although a size 5 can become a size 6 and a size 6 a size 7, the doctor cannot turn a size 3 penis into a size 10. It just will not happen. However, if one has the money and the inclination, these procedures may be the ticket for immediate, if modest, gains in phallic dimensions.

Actually, much more needs to be learned about the long-term repercussions of surgical enlargement. We need to know the psychological effects on the male and his partner, how lasting the results are, potential side-effects and complications, and its long term merits. Stay tuned.

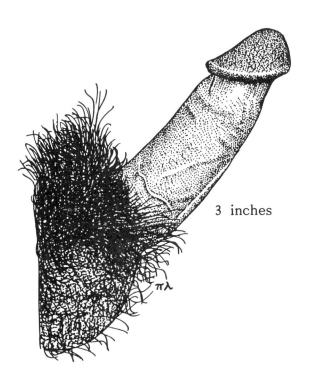

3 inches

πλ

❑   Don't be deceived. A number of porn movies have recently been issued featuring men with 16-18" organs. These are clearly fakes and are easy to spot. Look for leather harnesses which are used to hold the penis against the body. Real penises don't need harnesses.

178

8

Parting shots

─────────────────────────

Apologia

On occasion, I receive letters from readers who express disapproval at my perceived bias toward the large phallus. They claim that this subject only serves to increase their anxiety over their modest dimensions.

This book is not meant to be an indictment of the small penis. Quite the contrary. The male organ is a beautiful and fascinating creation in all its multifarious shapes, sizes, and colors. However, societal approbation has glorified the large phallus and has made it THE physical standard by which virility is judged, on par with tall stature, deep voices, bulging muscles, and hairy chests. Men that possess one or more of these uniquely male characteristics are perceived to be more masculine.

There is no denying that a larger penis is secretly desired by most men. Physicians and marital counselors are continually assuaging the fears of their clients with smaller penises, and advice columns are more frequently addressing this very issue. Still, men modestly hide their genitals behind crumpled towels in the locker room for fear that they might be perceived as "less of a man."

───────────────────────────────

❏ In the 1970s, an underground tabloid was published which listed hundreds of celebrities along with their penis size. This hard-to-find publication is now a collector's item.

179

Twenty five years ago, this taboo subject was a villainous bugbear for millions of men who had no access to reliable information regarding penis size and function. Fortunately, the sexual and information revolutions have begun to open up discussion into this terra incognita, and finally, books such as this are providing hard-to-find information for the male who is interested in improving his sexual performance and perhaps increasing the size of his penis. And that is the sole purpose of this book.

This book culminates in the simple question--does penis size matter? This question has a simple answer. If penis size is important to you or to your partner, then it is indeed important. On the other hand, if you are currently satisfied with the size of your organ, then penis size is NOT important. Indeed, many women experience extreme discomfort with an outsized organ. In such a case, a smaller or average sized organ does the job better than a large penis. Remember what the Taoists say about penis size--that it must be paired with a vagina of equivalent dimensions in order for sexual harmony to ensue.

Now for a theory that may surprise you. From my research it appears that most men want a larger penis to impress other men. This may sound like an oddly-modulated premise, especially for a heterosexual man, but indeed, a larger penis establishes his position on the totem pole of virility. And heterosexual men do indeed compete with each other in all areas of life. Cock size is no exception. Whether or not there is any factual basis to the premise, the truth is that men still believe that a larger penis makes him more sexually-desirable and virile. An otherwise unimpressive male can suddenly elevate himself high on that totem pole when his outsized penis is revealed in the locker room. You may recall the example of the hugely-endowed man who entered the steam room at the beginning of this book. When dressed in street clothes, no one paid any attention to the man who was likely brushed off as an inconsequential milquetoast. His pendulous penis, however, quickly upstaged the jocks and athletes in the sauna. This is a phenomenon I call "the sudden stud factor." Although many women do express a preference for a larger penis, they are not as phallus conscious as men. Most still adhere to the "technique over size" philosophy of sex. Men, however, are very aware of each other in the shower and how they measure up. Without a doubt, a large penis can go a long way to bolstering a man's sense of self-esteem and pride.

❏   The testicles of the blue whale average 2 1/2 feet long (.85 m) and weigh about 110 lbs. (50 kg).

180

When you're ready for a larger penis

Once you decide to pursue your goal of a larger penis, several points should be kept in mind. Remember that success in any endeavor (whether it be a career goal, athletic objective, or penis enlargement) is no accident. Anthony Robbins, the author of *Personal Power*, has crystallized the ultimate success formula in four simple steps:

1) Know your desired outcome (in this case, a larger penis)

2) Get yourself to take action by deciding to do so

3) Notice what you're getting from your actions

4) If what you're doing is not working, change your approach

For those of you who are impatient and want to accelerate the pace of your success, here are three steps used by successful people in all walks of life:

1) Find someone who is already getting the results you want. In this case--a man who has already increased the size of his penis.

2) Find out specifically what that person is doing.

3) Follow the same steps and you'll achieve the same results.

You'll find that if you apply this simple model to ANY endeavor, you will achieve success. When I first became interested in the possibility of penis enlargement in 1985, I read all the books I could get my hands on (which were few and far between), I talked to physicians (many laughed), and sent away for the gadgets found in the back pages of sleazy adult magazines that promised a larger penis. Yes, virtually all of them were meretricious scams designed to get me to part with my money. But eventually, through my persistence, I located a couple of men who had developed large, lush cocks through vacuum pumping. This underground network soon put me into contact with dozens of others who shared the same enlargement obsession.

Through this pool of shared resources, I was able to collect and distill useful information. I finally stumbled upon an outfit in England that promoted a "scientifically-proven" method of penis enlargement. Even with a stiff $100 pricetag, the offer was too enticing to pass up. Once I received the kit, I proceeded to undertake the course with obsessive abandon. Disconcerted

---

❏ In Great Britain, circumcision rates once topped 90%. Once socialized medicine stopped paying for routine circumcisions, the rate dropped dramatically. Now less than 10% of British male infants are circumcised.

that I had not gained any appreciable length, I persevered nevertheless. Whereas the course alleged that most men noticed permanent results within 100 days, it took me nearly 4 months to gain 1/2" (1.3 cm) in length. After a year of near daily workouts, I achieved my goal of a 1" (2.5 cm) increase in length. I was elated. I offer this anecdote as encouragement to those of you who are interested in a similar goal.

As a final word, whether you choose surgical enlargement for immediate increases, or a manual method that you can do in the privacy of your own home, make sure that you are well-informed beforehand. Read any and all information you can on the subject and talk to others who have engaged in penis enlargement. You will find these by asking your penis enlargement surgeon to provide phone contacts to his satisfied patients. You will also find them by perusing the personal ads in adult publications. Your best source for up-to-the-minute information on enlargement, however, is *Penis Power Quarterly,* the only journal that specializes in news regarding genital enlargement and enhancement. See the back of the book for subscription information.

As you pursue your enlargement regimen, I welcome your correspondence, photos, and observations. Let me know of your experiences, your successes, and of other methods you come across. All the best.

Gary Griffin

100 S. Sunrise Way, Suite #484

Palm Springs, CA 92262

MARCH OF COCKS

In the next five pages, we'll showcase six different penises, starting with an average-sized 6-incher (15 cm) and increasing in 1" (2.5 cm) increments until we arrive at a pendulous 11-incher (28 cm). This "march of cocks" will graphically show the difference that an inch can make.

❑ The 70s rock group 10 cc *(I'm not in love, The things we do for love)* took their name from what they thought was the volume of male ejaculate. Actually, the average male only ejaculates half that amount.

Six Inches (15 cm)

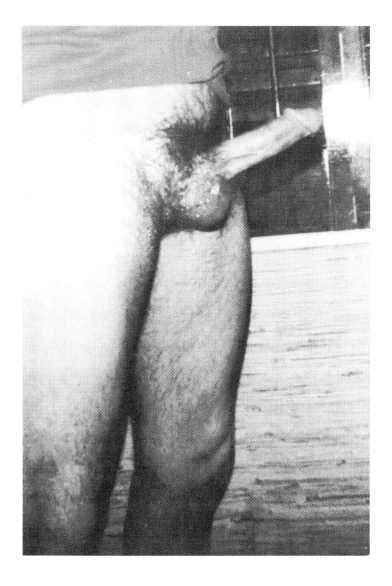

An average-sized penis. 75% of all adult males measure within an inch of this size.

Seven inches (18 cm)

This young man has a good reason to smile. With an impressively thick 7" (18 cm) penis, only 15% of all men measure this size or larger.

Eight inches (20 cm)

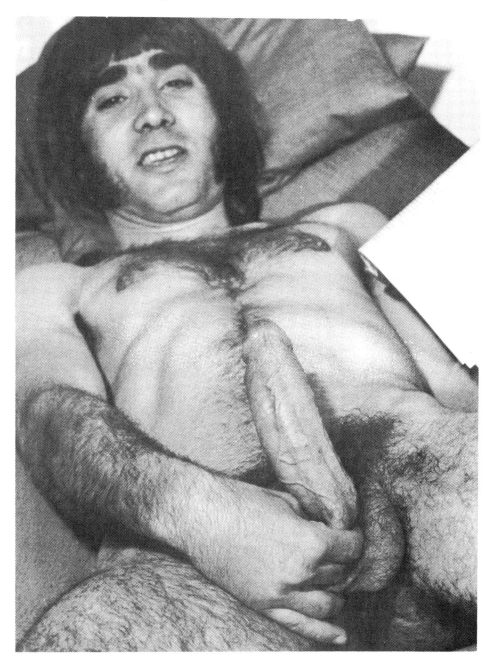

This Italian man sports a penis size found in only 3% of the male population.

Nine Inches (23 cm)

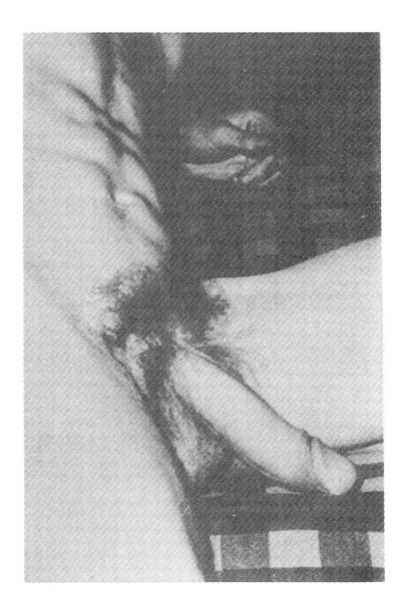

A penis this size is extremely rare, being found in perhaps 2 men in 1,000.

Ten inches (25 cm)

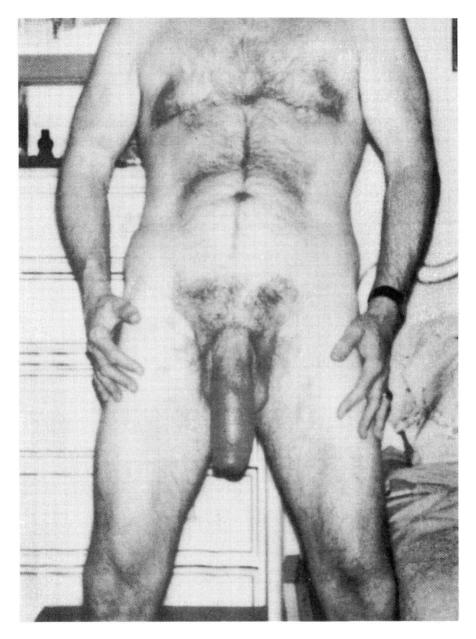

When erect, this horse-sized penis measures an incredible 10". A penis this large is so rare that it is possessed by less than 1 in 10,000 men.

Eleven Inches (28 cm)

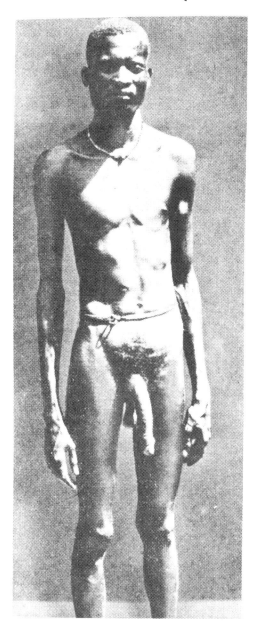

The stupendous penis on this Watusi tribesman measures 11" when flaccid and an incredible foot long (30 cm) when erect. According to statistical models, there are less than 5,000 penises of this size in the world.

Bibliography

Baldwin, Dorothy, "Male Sexual Health," Hippocrene Books, NYC, NY, 1991.

Biddle-Barrow, Sidney, "Mayflower Madam," 1985.

Bosch, Vernon, "Sexual Dimensions--The Fact & Fiction of Genital Size," Helios Press, 1979.

Brooks, William, "How to enlarge your penis," House One, 1979.

Burton, Sir Richard, "The Arabian Nights,"

Chang, Dr. Stephen T., "The Tao of Sexology," Tao Publishing, San Francisco, CA, 1986.

Chang, Dr. Stephen T., "The Book of internal Exercises," Strawberry Hill Press, San Francisco, CA, 1978.

Chase, Dr. Gifford, "Sex in the fast lane,"

Danoff, M.D., Dudley Seth, "Superpotency,"

Evans, M. Erick, "The Phallus in history and fact!", Guild Press Ltd., 1969.

Friday, Nancy, "My Secret Garden--Women's Sexual Fantasies,"

Goldstein, Irwin, and Rothstein, Larry, "The Potent Male," Price, Stern, Sloan, Los Angeles, CA, 1990.

Grange, Dr. Felix, "The Male Genital Organs and their Improvement," Roberts Publications.

Keuls, Eva C., "The Reign of the Phallus," Harper & Rowe, 1985

Knight, Richard Payne, and Wright, Thomas, "A History of Phallic Worship," Dorset Press, NY, 1990.

Kokken, Dr. Shak, "A Happier Sex Life,"

McCarthy, Dr. Barry, "Male sexual awareness,"

Parsons, Alexandra, "Facts & Phalluses" St. Martin's Press, NY, 1990.

Purvis, M.D., Phd, Kenneth, "The Male Sexual Machine," St. Martin's Press, NYC, NY, 1992.

Richards, M.D., Brian, "The Penis," Valentine Products, 1977.

Roles, Stephen, "The Human Aphrodisiac," Baby Shoe Publications, Sandwich, Kent, England, 1986.

Rubin, Dr. David, "Everything you always wanted to know about sex, but were afraid to ask," 1969.

Rutledge, Leigh W., "The Gay Book of Lists," Alison Publications, 1987.

Schwartz, Kit, "The Male Member," St. Martin's Press, NYC, NY, 1985.

Simons, G.L., "The Illustrated Book of Sexual Records," Bell Publishing, NYC, NY, 1974.

Strage, Mark, "The Durable Fig Leaf," Dorset Press, NYC, NY, 1980.

Tannahill, Reay, "Sex in History," Scarborough House, 1980.

Thorn, Dr. Mark, "Taboo no more--The Phallus in fact, fantasy, and fiction," Shapolsky Publishers, NYC, NY, 1990.

Van de Velde, M.D., Thomas, "Ideal Marriage," 1930.

Walton, Alan Hull, "Aphrodisiacs--From Legend to Prescription,"

Welch, Leslee, "The Complete Book of Sexual Trivia," Citadel Press, NYC, NY, 1992.

Zacks, Richard, "History Laid Bare," HarperCollins Publishers, NYC, NY, 1994.

Index

Other books by Gary Griffin

☐ **"Penis Power--A Complete Guide to Potency Restoration",** ✓ 10-1-97
  ISBN #1-879967-08-1. 120 pages. $9.95.

☐ **"Testicles--The Ball Book,"**
  ISBN #1-879967-09-X. 100 pages. $9.95.

☐ **"The Vacuum Pumper's Handbook,"** ✓   10-1-97
  ISBN #1-879967-07-3. 100 pages. $9.95.

☐ **"Straight talk about Surgical Penis Enlargement,"**
  ISBN #1-879967-12-X. 100 pages. $9.95.

☐ **"The Condom Encyclopedia,"**
  ISBN #1-879967-14-6. 128 pages. $9.95.

☐ **"The Art of Auto Fellatio,"**
  ISBN #1-879967-11-1. 100 pages. $9.95.

The closet 12-30-97 ☐ **"The Horsemen's Club--True Tales of Legendary Endowments,"**
  ISBN #1-879967-10-3. 100 pages. $9.95.

☐ **"Aphrodisiacs for Men,"**
  ISBN #1-879967-03-3. 64 pages. $9.95. ✓   10-1-97

☐ **"The History of Men's Underwear,"**
  ISBN #1-879967-06-5. 80 pages. $9.95.

☐ **"Decircumcision--Foreskin Restoration Methods,"**
  ISBN #1-879967-05-7. 112 pages. $9.95.

For a free brochure or to order any of the above titles, send the proper amount plus
$2 per book for postage to:

Added Dimensions Publishing

100 S. Sunrise Way, Suite #484

Palm Springs, CA 90062

4216 Beverly Blvd Suite 262
L.A. Ca. 90004
12-18-97

Penis Power Quarterly

The world's first journal that reports the latest research into male genital enlargement and sexual health. Published four times a year, here are some of the topics covered in recent issues:

- ❑ Interviews with the world's most prominent penis enlargement surgeons
- ❑ Before and after photos of surgical enlargement
- ❑ The sensational South African "Project P" which can add 2-8 cm. to your penis
- ❑ Effective drugs for treating premature ejaculation
- ❑ Complete product review of all vacuum pump products on the market
- ❑ Special device worn on the penis that restores the foreskin while lengthening the penis
- ❑ Secret aphrodisiac formulas which ignite red-hot passions in men!
- ❑ The man's "G-spot" and how to stimulate it
- ❑ Powerful new injections for instant erections
- ❑ Specialty underwear with expandable pouches for men with large genitals
- ❑ The hypnotist that has developed a protocol for enlarging the penis through auto-suggestion
- ❑ The incredible baldness cure that really works--available now in Canada!

AND MUCH MORE. Each issue is loaded with the latest research into male sexuality and contains uncensored photos of "PPQ" readers with incredible endowments. "PPQ" publishes articles on subjects that are considered too taboo by other publications. This is information that is unavailable anywhere else at any price. Find out why over 50 physicians subscribe to "PPQ." An annual subscription of four issues is $24.95 ($35 outside the U.S. and Canada). Mailed in a plain envelope. Send to:

Added Dimensions Publishing
100 S. Sunrise Way, Suite #484
Palm Springs, CA 92263

10-197

About the author

Gary Griffin is a California native who lives in Palm Springs. He studied biology at Brigham Young University and received his MBA from UCLA. Listed in "Who's Who in the West" and "Men of Distinction," Gary is the founder of the "American Association of Phalloplasty Augmentation Surgeons" and a member of the "Society for the Scientific Study of Sex." In 1987, he established "Added Dimensions Publishing" which is dedicated to publishing the latest research in male sexuality. He has appeared on dozens of talkshows across the U.S.

His latest project is an extensive linguistics research compendium entitled *The World's Top 100 Languages*. A traveler with terminal wanderlust, Gary has lived in the U.S., Sweden, and Thailand, and speaks six languages. A dedicated vegetarian, conservationist, and animal lover, he enjoys Scuba diving, cross-country skiing, college football, and bodysurfing.